MUSCLE MEETS MAGNET

Per A. Tesch

MUSCLE MEETS MAGNET

Produced and Published by
PA TESCH AB
Stockholm, Sweden

Barbells and dumbbells were provided by ELEIKO AB, Halmstad, Sweden.
US address:
DYNAMIC FITNESS EQUIPMENT, P.O. Box 2866, Livolia, MI 48151

Photographer: Per Bernal

Cover design and book layout:
Ed Passarelli / BODY COMP Art Direction & Design
1128 Ocean Park Blvd. Suite 310, Santa Monica, CA 90405

Cover models: Stephan Haertl and Robby Timonen (inset)

Exercise models:
Lisbeth Wikström, Swedish Champion and Stephan Haertl, M.Sc.,
European and German Heavy Weight Champion

MUSCLE MEETS MAGNET ISBN 91-630-2391-1

Distributor:
BOOKMASTERS, INC.
1444 U.S. Rt. 42
RD 11
Mansfield, Ohio 44903

$19.95 plus $4.95 check or money order, or use Master Card/VISA and call
800-247-6553. Ohio resident add 6% sales tax.
Foreign orders by mail must be in US currency drawn on a US bank and shipping extra
(North America add $5.00, all others add $15.00).

TABLE OF CONTENTS

Dedication

To those who introduced me to sports

and the science of exercise.

BACKGROUND

Wouldn't it be great to look inside your arm and see which of the three heads of the triceps brachii (the elbow extensor muscle group) was used in the Military press? This book shows you that the long head is not used to do the Military press! You know the best way to stress the soleus muscle in the back of the calf is Seated Calf Raises. Now you can see it! Would you believe that the hamstrings muscles in the back of the thigh are not the ones really stretched as you lower into that deep squat? It is the powerful adductor muscles of the thigh that are really pulled, and you will see this. By viewing this book, you will see which specific exercises for the arms and legs can be used to develop individual muscles, even parts of them, like never before. If you want to train smart, do the right exercises for that specific muscle, see which different exercises can and cannot be used to train that specific muscle, this is the book for you.

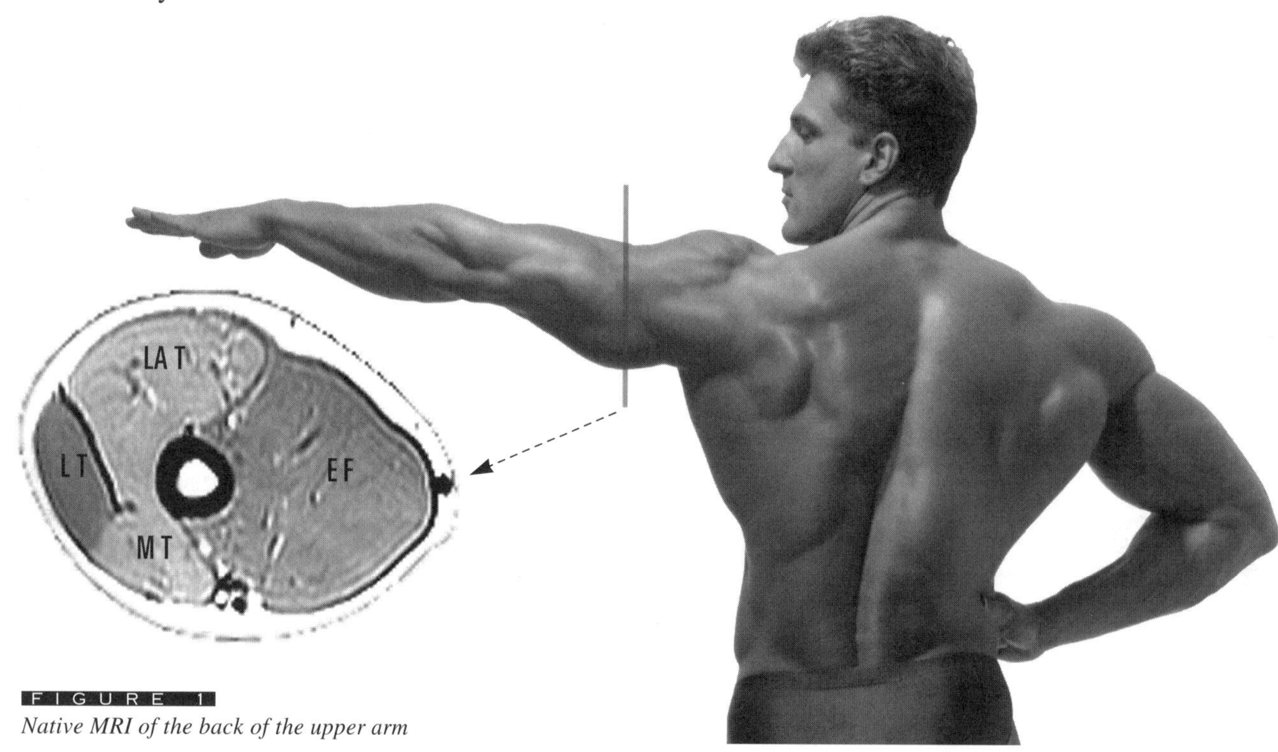

FIGURE 1
Native MRI of the back of the upper arm

What does this book provide that is so new? Why is it different than the fifty or so other bodybuilding books on the market? A powerful new technology, magnetic resonance imaging (MRI), was used to definitively show you which individual muscles are used to do different bodybuilding exercises. No more guesswork based on where a muscle starts and stops. Oh, it goes across this joint, so it must do this. No, this book is much different.

MRI is the most advanced technology available today for visualization of soft tissue inside the human body. An MR image of the left, upper arm shows individual muscles with remarkable clarity (Figure 1).

This MRI is a slice taken where the line is drawn across the bodybuilder's left, upper arm. To get oriented to the image, hold your left arm out like he is, and imagine looking into a slice of it. The "python", that large vein which runs down the middle of your biceps, is evident on the right side of the image as a black dot. In the middle of the image, there is a black donut shaped object. This is the bone of your upper arm, the humerus. Now look at the muscle tissue! The elbow flexors (E F) are on the right side of the humerus, and appear dark gray. The long head (L T) of the triceps brachii appears on the far right of the image and is also dark gray. The lateral (LA T) and medial (M T) heads of the triceps brachii, however, are much lighter. They are "lit up" because this MRI of the left, upper arm was taken after 5 sets of ten repetitions of the Military press exercise had been performed with a load that gave a pretty good pump. While the mechanism for this contrast shift, this change in color, is not known, it is accepted that this occurred because these two heads of the triceps brachii were used to do the exercise. The long head (L T) was not used and remained dark gray, even though this exercise requires extensive elbow extension. The elbow flexors (E F) were also not used (remained dark gray) because they do not help with elbow extension. The take home message is, you cannot use the Military press to train the long head of the triceps brachii.

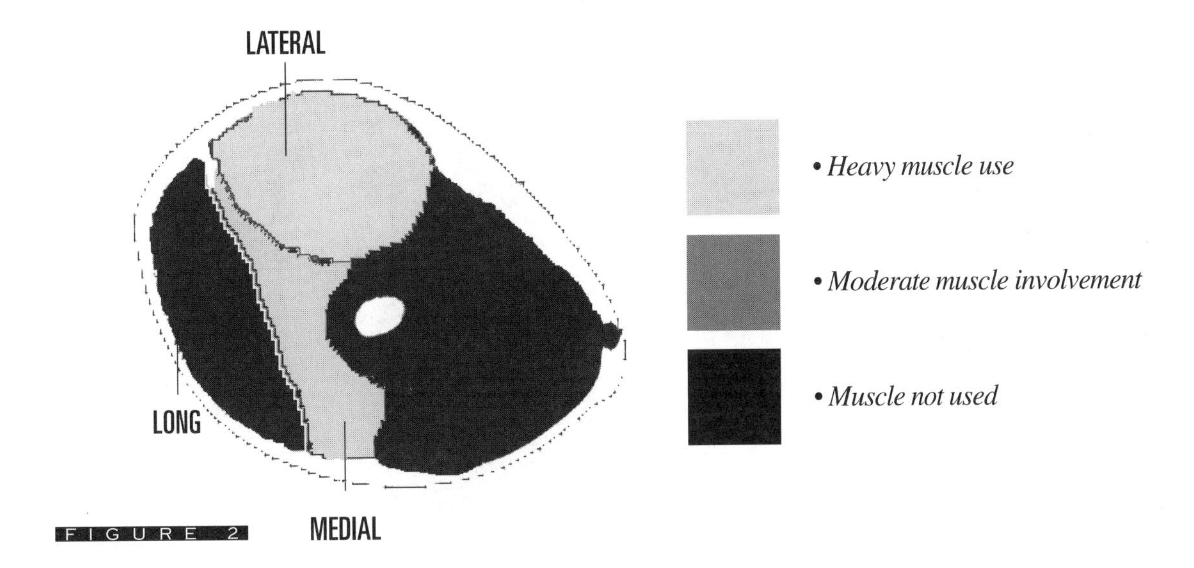

FIGURE 2

The pattern and extent of muscle use have been partitioned into three different levels of gray for the remainder of the book so you can easily see the most important thing, which individual muscles are used to do a given exercise. Light gray means heavy use was required during the exercise, medium gray indicates moderate involvement and dark gray means the muscle was not used. When shades of gray are applied to the muscles of Figure 1, the LATERAL and MEDIAL heads of the triceps brachii appear light gray because they are really taxed by the Military press (Figure 2). The LONG head and the forearm flexors are shaded dark because they contribute little to this exercise. No muscles appear medium gray in this image because none were moderately involved in this exercise.

This is the first report, using the "state of the art technology of MRI," to show in detail which muscles are used in the most important arm and leg exercises performed by bodybuilders. Experienced bodybuilders performed a variety of common exercises to the level of getting a good pump; five sets of ten to twelve repetitions. Then, using the magnet it was possible to "look inside" their bodies to see which muscles were used to do the exercise. Concentration was on exercises for the back and front of the upper arm, thigh and calf. Not every arm and leg exercise ever used in bodybuilding has been examined - but a lot of the more common ones.

Sit back, relax and enjoy this remarkable visual journey inside the human body to see what your muscles do, and good training.

GUIDE TO BODY ORIENTATION OF MRI'S

UPPER ARM GUIDE

LATERAL, LONG and MEDIAL heads of the triceps brachii and the **ELBOW FLEXORS** of the biceps brachii and brachialis muscles.

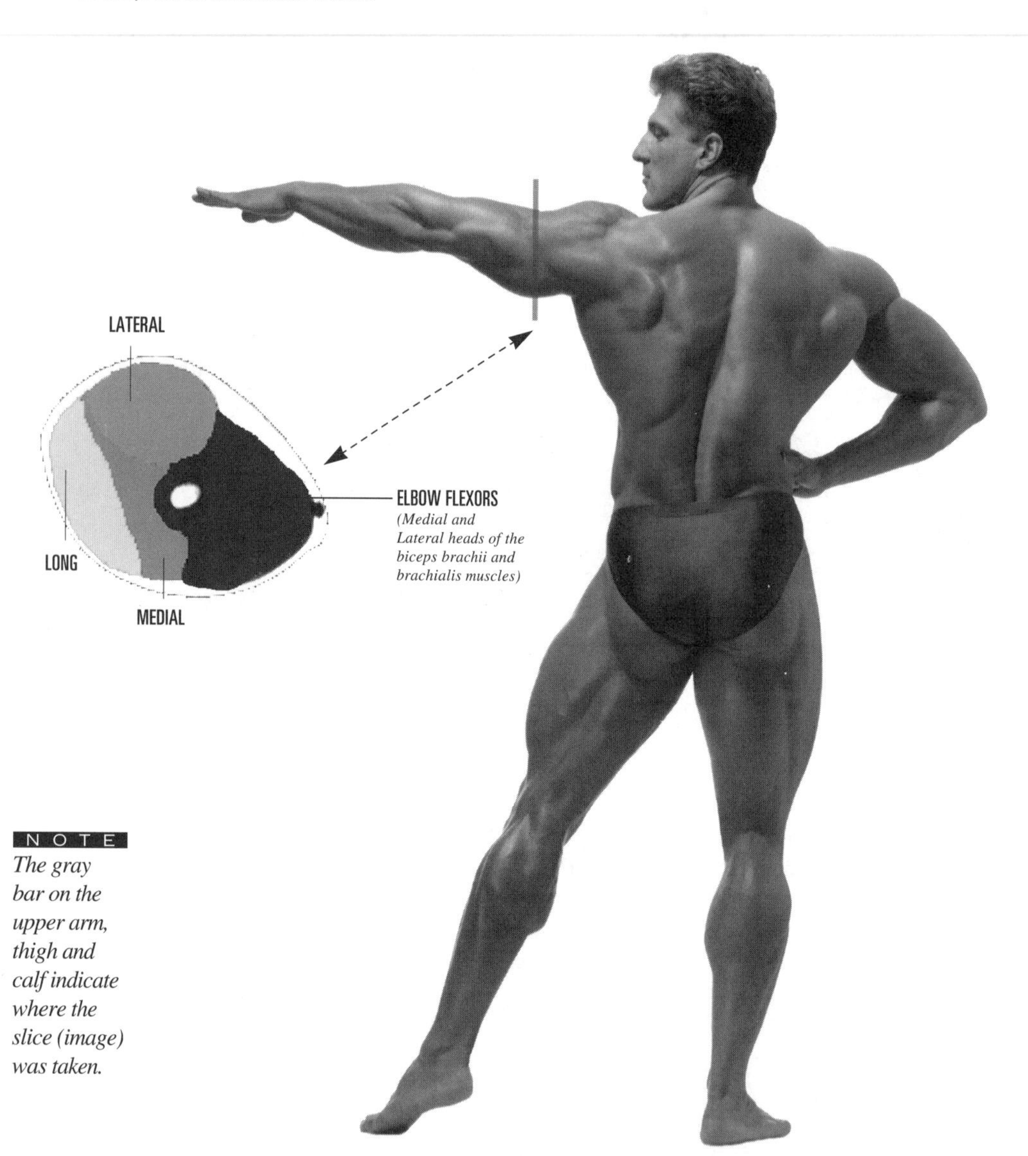

NOTE

The gray bar on the upper arm, thigh and calf indicate where the slice (image) was taken.

BACK AND FRONT OF UPPER ARM

Raise your left arm up to beside your body, palm down, and imagine looking into a slice (cross-section) of it. Always view the images from this perspective. If the bodybuilder is facing you while doing the exercise, just put yourself in his/her place, and visualize the image being taken of your left upper arm.

THIGH GUIDE

AD B=Adductor brevis
AD L=Adductor longus
AD M=Adductor magnus
BF=Biceps femoris
GR=Gracilis
RF=Rectus femoris
SR=Sartorius
ST=Semitendinosus
VM=Vastus medialis
VL=Vastus lateralis
VI=Vastus intermedius

CALF GUIDE

SO=Soleus
MG=Medial gastrocnemius
LG=Lateral gastrocnemius
TA=Tibialis anterior
TP=Tibialis posterior
PO=Popliteus
EDL=Extensor digitorum longus
PL=Peroneus longus

THIGH

Stand, look down at your right leg, and imagine looking into a slice (cross-section) of your right thigh. If the bodybuilder is facing you while doing the exercise, just put yourself in his/her place, and visualize the image being taken of your right thigh.

CALF

Stand, look down at your left leg, and imagine looking into a slice (cross-section) of your left calf. If the bodybuilder is facing you while doing the exercise, just put yourself in his/her place, and visualize the image being taken of your left calf.

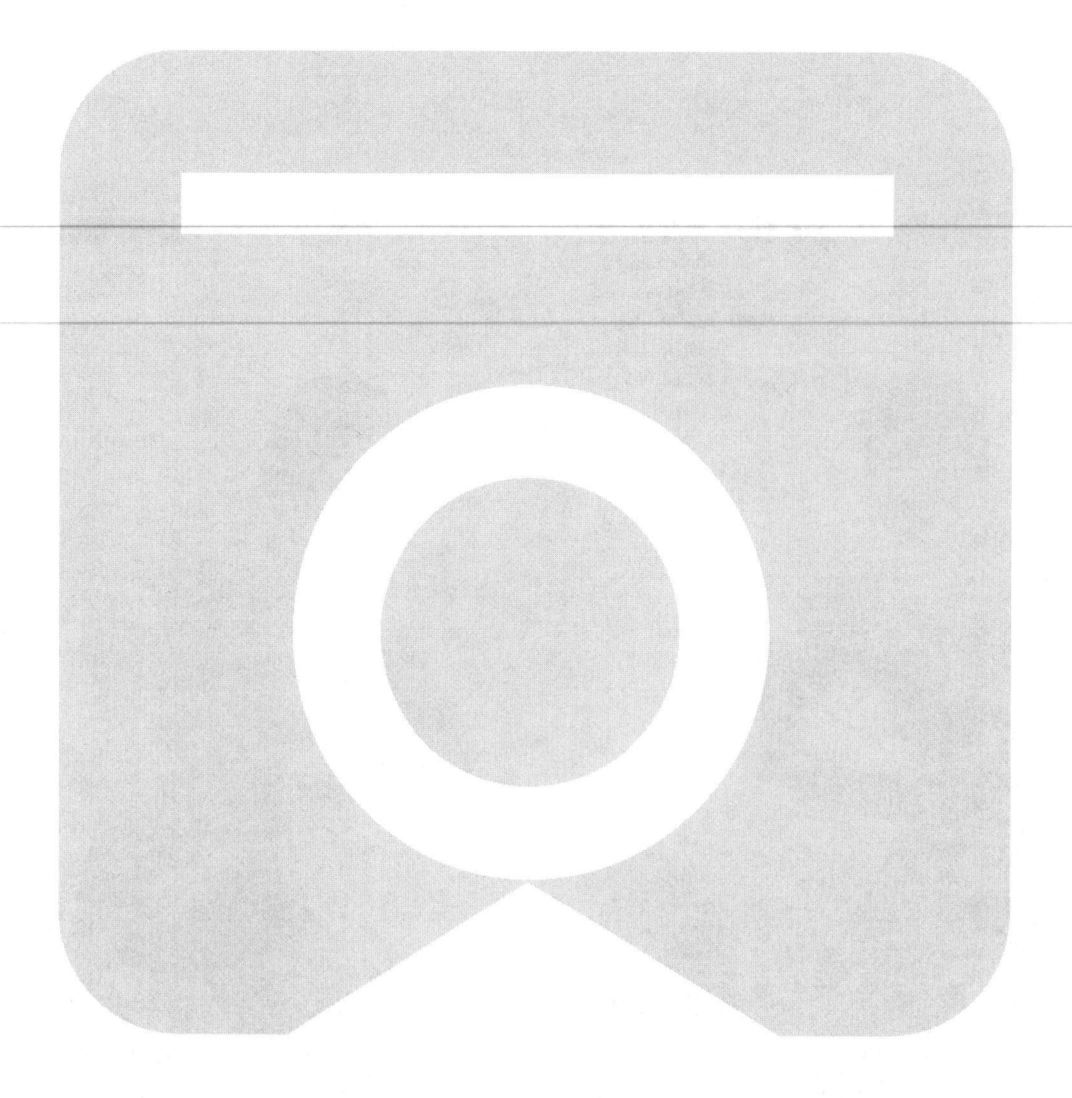

MRI

BACK OF THE UPPER ARM

1 FRENCH PRESS *with EZ bar.*

In the starting position, hold the EZ bar on the inside with arms extended directly over chest, the grip is midway between neutral and palm up. The bar is lowered to the forehead by flexing at the elbows, and after a short pause, raised to the starting position by extending at the elbows. This is not close grip benches or overhead flies, so keep the elbows stationary, held close together.

START

FINISH

MUSCLE FUNCTION

The French press with an EZ bar places marked emphasis on the long head of the triceps brachii. The medial and lateral heads of the triceps brachii are important, as indicated by their moderate use.

GUIDE

LATERAL, LONG and MEDIAL heads of triceps brachii.

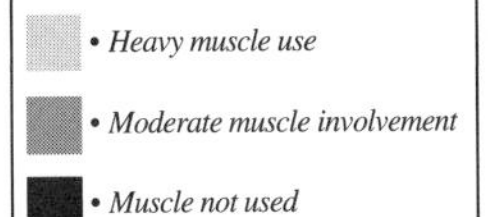

The muscles of the front of the upper arm appear black because they do not contribute to the exercise. Raise your left arm up to beside of your body, palm down, and imagine looking into a slice (cross-section) of your left upper arm.

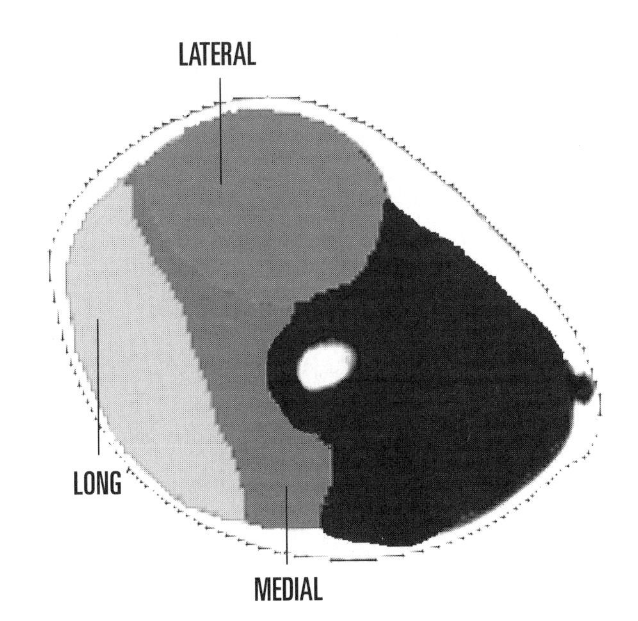

2 FRENCH PRESS *with EZ bar on decline bench.*

This is similar to exercise #1, except that it is done on a decline bench. The feet are higher than the head, in this example six inches.

MUSCLE FUNCTION

Doing the French press with an EZ bar in the decline position appears to allow for a greater range of motion about the elbow joint which necessitates marked use of not only the LONG HEAD, but also the MEDIAL and LATERAL HEADS of the triceps brachii.

GUIDE

LATERAL, LONG and MEDIAL heads of triceps brachii.

The muscles of the front of the upper arm appear black because they do not contribute to the exercise. Raise your left arm up to beside of your body, palm down, and imagine looking into a slice (cross-section) of your left, upper arm.

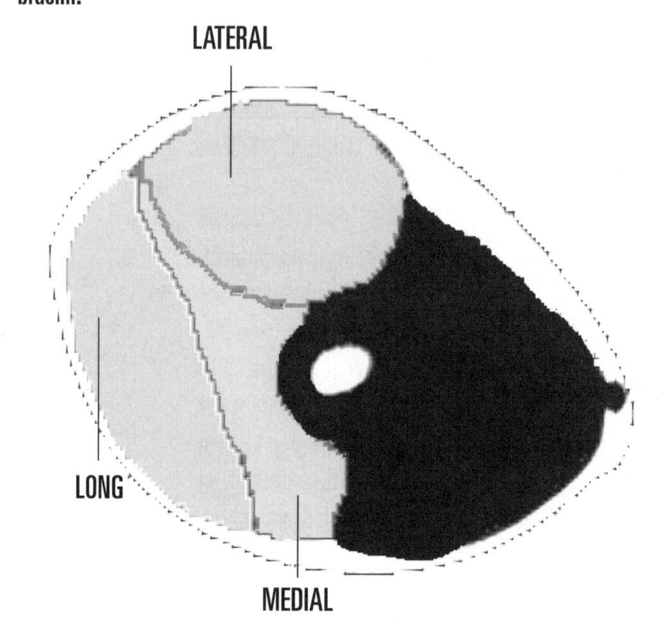

3 SUPINE TRICEPS EXTENSION *with dumbbell and neutral grip.*

This exercise is just like # 1 (French press with EZ bar and narrow grip), except dumbbells are used with palms facing each other. The dumbbells are lowered as far as possible beside the head. This is not dumbbell flies or dumbbell bench press, so keep the elbows stationary, held close together.

MUSCLE FUNCTION

The slight internal rotation of the palm, and having to balance the weight with one arm emphasizes stress of the LATERAL HEAD of the triceps brachii. The medial and long heads are not left out, they show moderate use.

GUIDE

LATERAL, LONG and MEDIAL heads of triceps brachii.

The muscles of the front of the upper arm appear black because they do not contribute to the exercise. Raise your left arm up to beside of your body, palm down, and imagine looking into a slice (cross-section) of your left, upper arm.

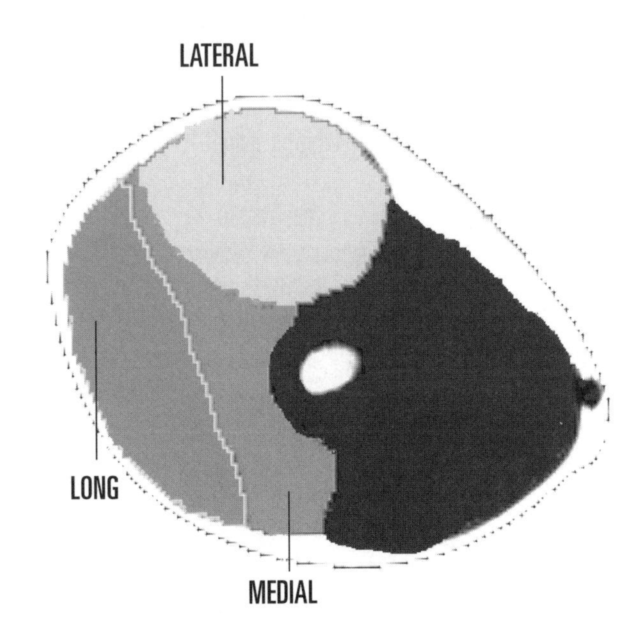

4 OVERHEAD TRICEPS EXTENSION *with dumbbell and neutral grip.*

Raise dumbbell directly over head to where the arm is extended to achieve the starting position. Using the neutral grip, lower dumbbell in smooth fashion behind the head as far as possible by flexing at the elbow. Pause, and now raise the dumbbell to the starting position by contracting the elbow extensors. Remember, keep the upper arm vertical to the floor and directly beside the head. This is not a pressing exercise.

MUSCLE FUNCTION

This exercise allows a marked range of motion about the elbow joint, and a fair amount of weight can be used with the neutral grip. To accomplish this exercise, ALL THREE HEADS of the triceps brachii are markedly stressed.

GUIDE

LATERAL, LONG and MEDIAL heads of triceps brachii.

The muscles of the front of the upper arm appear black because they do not contribute to the exercise. Raise your left arm up to beside of your body, palm down, and imagine looking into a slice (cross-section) of your left, upper arm.

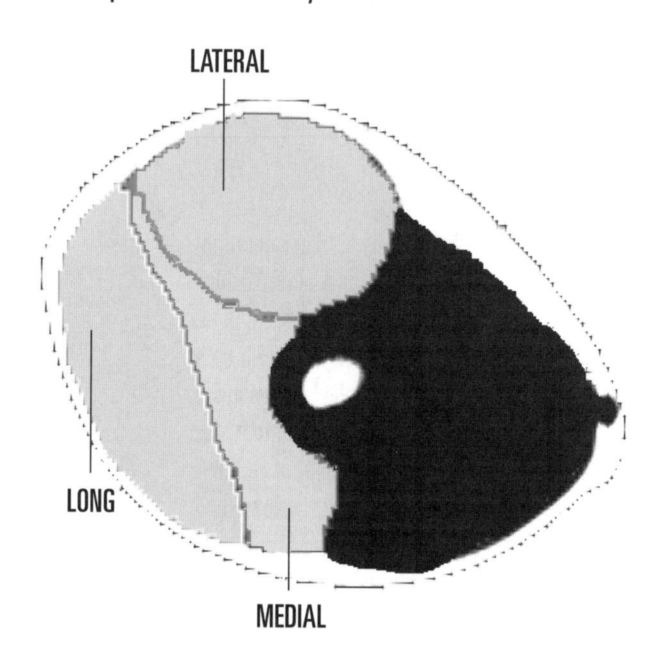

5 OVERHEAD TRICEPS EXTENSION *with dumbbell and rotation.*

This exercise is just like #4, except as the dumbbell passes by the head on the way up (elbow at about 90 degrees) the hand is rotated out so that the palm faces away from the body. With the palm facing away from the body, begin lowering the dumbbell in a smooth fashion by flexing at the elbow. As soon as movement starts, also begin to rotate the palm inward so that when the dumbbell passes the head (elbow at about 90 degrees) the hand is in the neutral position. Pause, and now raise the dumbbell to the starting position by contracting the elbow extensors. As the dumbbell passes the head, rotate the palm away from the body. Remember, keep the upper arm vertical to the floor and directly beside the head. This is not a pressing exercise.

START

FINISH

MUSCLE FUNCTION

As you can see, this exercise takes a lot out of ALL THREE HEADS of the triceps brachii.

GUIDE

LATERAL, LONG and MEDIAL heads of triceps brachii.

The muscles of the front of the upper arm appear black because they do not contribute to the exercise. Raise your left arm up to beside of your body, palm down, and imagine looking into a slice (cross-section) of your left, upper arm.

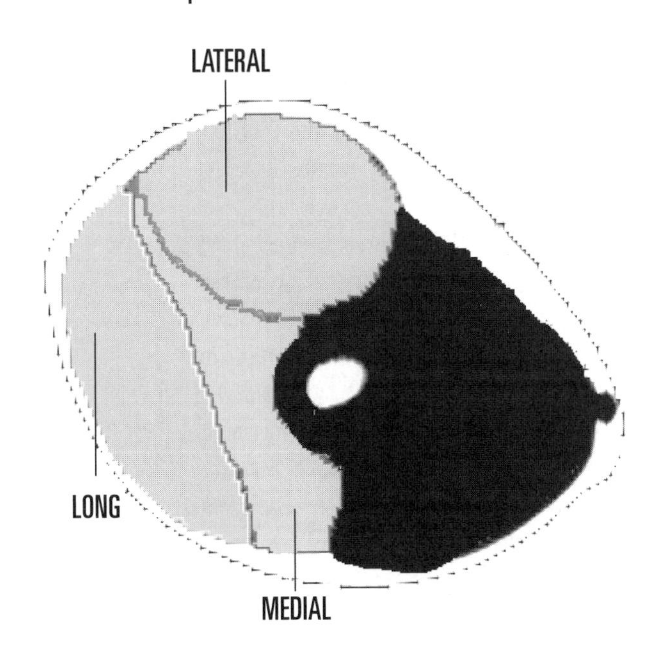

MRI

6 OVERHEAD TRICEPS EXTENSION *with reverse grip.*

Achieve starting position using a reverse grip. Lean slightly aside and use your hand on the bench for support. Keep dumbbell horizontal to floor throughout the movement, make sure the elbow is kept stationary and is extended at the starting position.

MUSCLE FUNCTION

Oh yeah, feel that stretch. This exercise also allows a decent range of motion about the elbow joint. The hand position, however, limits the amount of weight that can be used. The LONG HEAD is the only one that shows marked use. The medial and lateral heads of the triceps brachii provide moderate support.

GUIDE

LATERAL, LONG and MEDIAL heads of triceps brachii.

The muscles of the front of the upper arm appear black because they do not contribute to the exercise. Raise your left arm up to beside of your body, palm down, and imagine looking into a slice (cross-section) of your left, upper arm

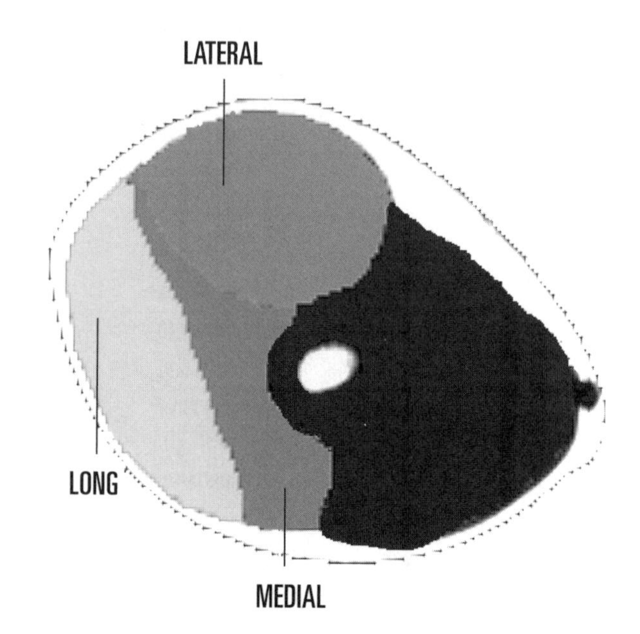

7 STANDING FRENCH PRESS *with straight bar.*

The idea is to keep the upper arms upright and parallel with the long axis of the body. The grip is shoulder width with the palms facing up. The bar is raised over the head by extending at the elbows. Extend until the bar is completely overhead, pause, and then lower the bar smoothly to the starting position.

MUSCLE FUNCTION

For this exercise, the **MEDIAL** and **LATERAL HEADS** of the triceps brachii do the majority of the work, with the long head providing some support.

GUIDE

LATERAL, LONG and MEDIAL heads of triceps brachii.

The muscles of the front of the upper arm appear black because they do not contribute to the exercise. Raise your left arm up to beside of your body, palm down, and imagine looking into a slice (cross-section) of your left, upper arm.

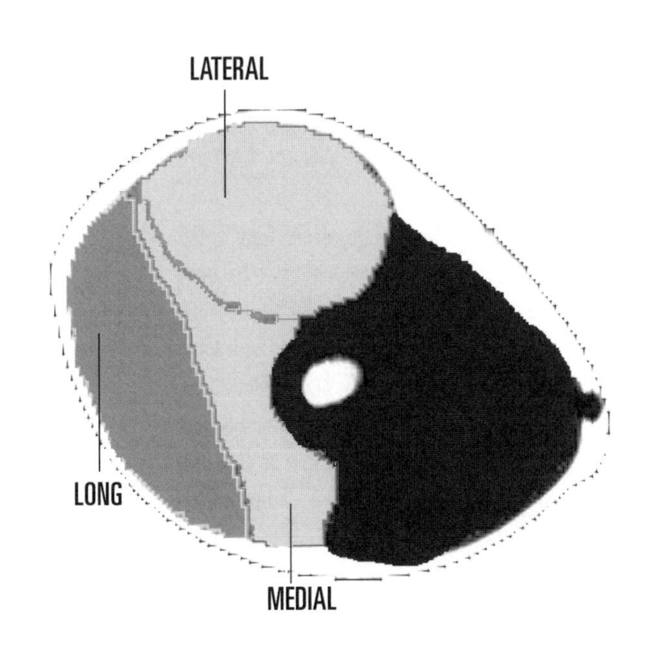

8 TRICEPS PUSH DOWN *with straight bar and narrow grip.*

This is a classic pulley machine exercise for developing the triceps. Start the exercise by contracting the triceps, thereby pushing the bar down until the arms are straight. After a short pause, relax somewhat and the weight will raise the bar. Remember, control this motion. Let the weight raise the bar until the elbows are flexed well beyond 90 degrees, and you will be back to the starting position. It is important to keep the elbows close to the side and immobile during the course of the exercise.

MUSCLE FUNCTION

So you want the horseshoe. This is one that will do it. Both the LONG and LATERAL HEADS of the triceps brachii get the job done in this case. The medial head is not left out, providing moderate assistance.

GUIDE

LATERAL, LONG and MEDIAL heads of triceps brachii.

The muscles of the front of the upper arm appear black because they do not contribute to the exercise. Raise your left arm up to beside of your body, palm down, and imagine looking into a slice (cross-section) of your left, upper arm.

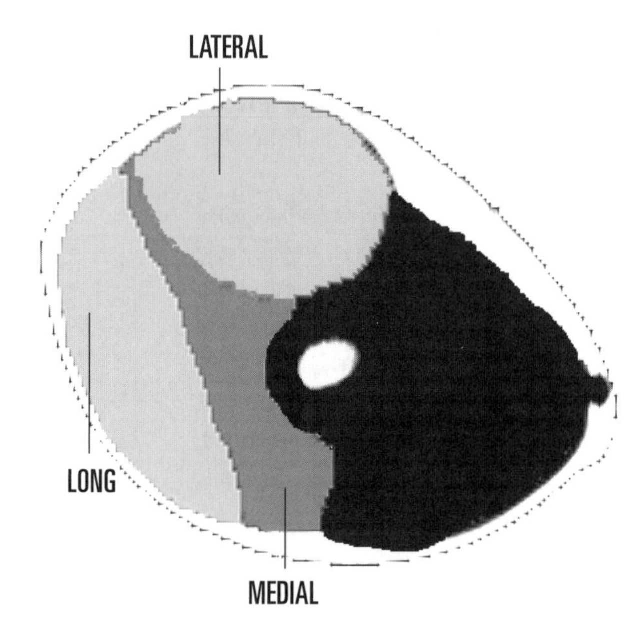

9 TRICEPS PUSH DOWN *with rope.*

This exercise is very similar to #8, except a rope is used which allows two things, 1) the exercise is started at the top with the hands essentially in the neutral position, and 2) during the course of the push down, the wrists are rotated inward such that at complete elbow extension the palms are facing down. As the weight pulls the rope back up the wrists are rotated such that at the top of the ascent, the hands are again in the neutral position.

MUSCLE FUNCTION

As some have put forth, adding that little twist at the bottom is all it takes. Now, ALL THREE HEADS of the triceps brachii are getting taxed to the max.

GUIDE

LATERAL, LONG and MEDIAL heads of triceps brachii.

The muscles of the front of the upper arm appear black because they do not contribute to the exercise. Raise your left arm up to beside of your body, palm down, and imagine looking into a slice (cross-section) of your left, upper arm.

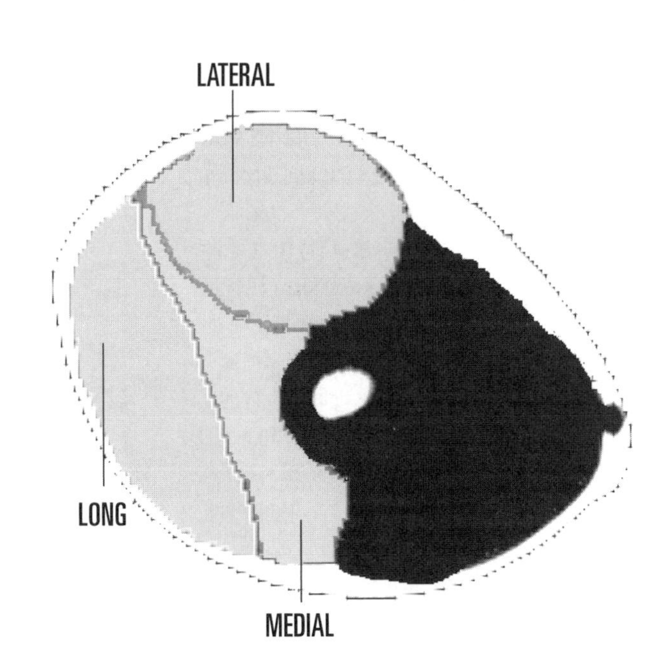

10 TRICEPS PUSH DOWN *with angled bar.*

This exercise is just like #9, except an angled bar is used to keep the grip just short of neutral.

MUSCLE FUNCTION

Again, it seems that getting the hand to the neutral position is one way of taxing ALL THREE HEADS of the triceps brachii to the maximum.

GUIDE

LATERAL, LONG and MEDIAL heads of triceps brachii.

The muscles of the front of the upper arm appear black because they do not contribute to the exercise. Raise your left arm up to beside of your body, palm down, and imagine looking into a slice (cross-section) of your left, upper arm.

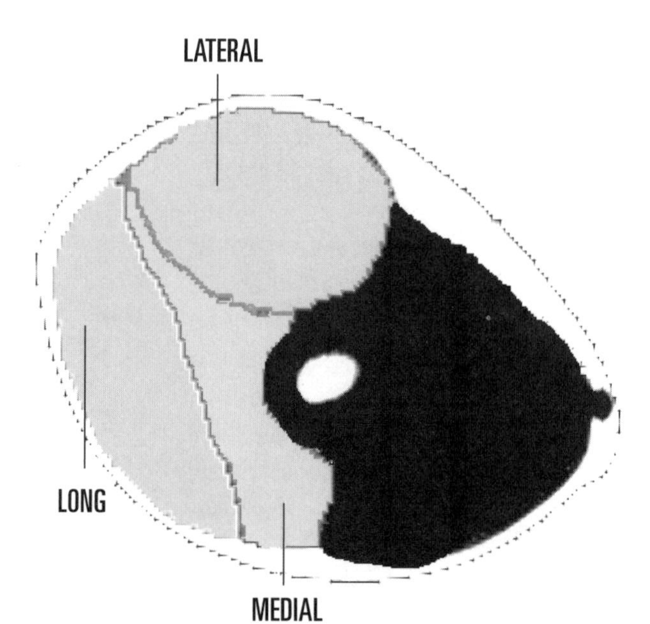

11 ONE ARM TRICEPS PUSH DOWN

Start the exercise by extending the elbow joint, thereby pushing the handle down until the arm is straight. After a short pause, relax somewhat and the weight will raise itself. Remember, control this motion. Let the weight raise the handle until the elbow is flexed beyond 90 degrees, and you will be back to the starting position. It is important to keep the elbow immobile during the course of the exercise. Keep the torso still, the upper arm in tight, and just use the triceps.

MUSCLE FUNCTION

As is obvious from the image, this exercise requires differential use of the three heads of the triceps brachii. Less emphasis is placed on the long head, while the MEDIAL and LATERAL HEADS take on the brunt of the work

GUIDE

LATERAL, LONG and MEDIAL heads of triceps brachii.

The muscles of the front of the upper arm appear black because they do not contribute to the exercise. Raise your left arm up to beside of your body, palm down, and imagine looking into a slice (cross-section) of your left, upper arm.

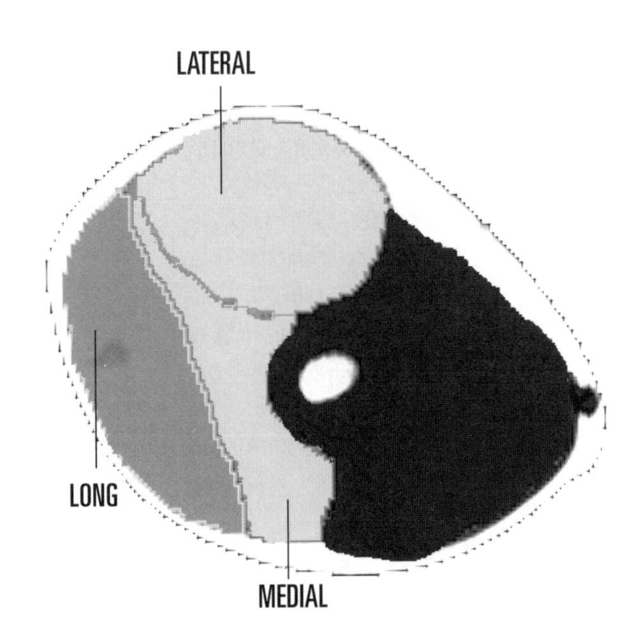

12 ONE ARM TRICEPS PUSH DOWN *with reverse grip.*

This is just like exercise #11, except that a reverse grip is used on the handle.

MUSCLE FUNCTION

Oh, do we feel weak. While not a lot of weight is used in this exercise, it seems to markedly tax ALL THREE HEADS of the triceps brachii.

GUIDE

LATERAL, LONG and MEDIAL heads of triceps brachii.

The muscles of the front of the upper arm appear black because they do not contribute to the exercise. Raise your left arm up to beside of your body, palm down, and imagine looking into a slice (cross-section) of your left, upper arm.

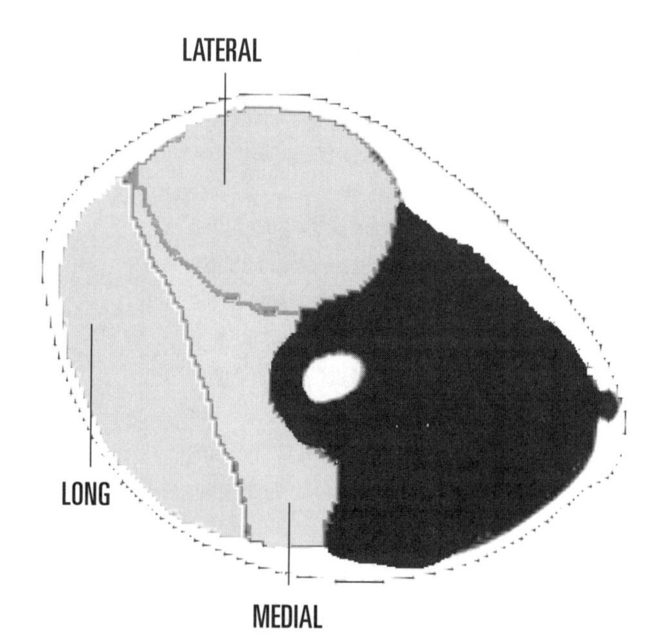

13 OVERHEAD TRICEPS EXTENSION *with rope.*

The most difficult part about this exercise may be getting into position to do it. During extension at the elbow joint be sure and keep the upper arms stationary beside the head. Try to eliminate any extraneous body movement, and complete the movement until full extension. After a short pause, relax, allowing the weight stack to descend which pulls the hands far behind the head to the starting position.

MUSCLE FUNCTION

If this exercise is difficult to do, the benefits should be worth it. This exercise really taxes the LATERAL HEAD of the triceps brachii, while some help is provided by its neighbors, the medial and long heads.

GUIDE

LATERAL, LONG and MEDIAL heads of triceps brachii.

The muscles of the front of the upper arm appear black because they do not contribute to the exercise. Raise your left arm up to beside of your body, palm down, and imagine looking into a slice (cross-section) of your left, upper arm.

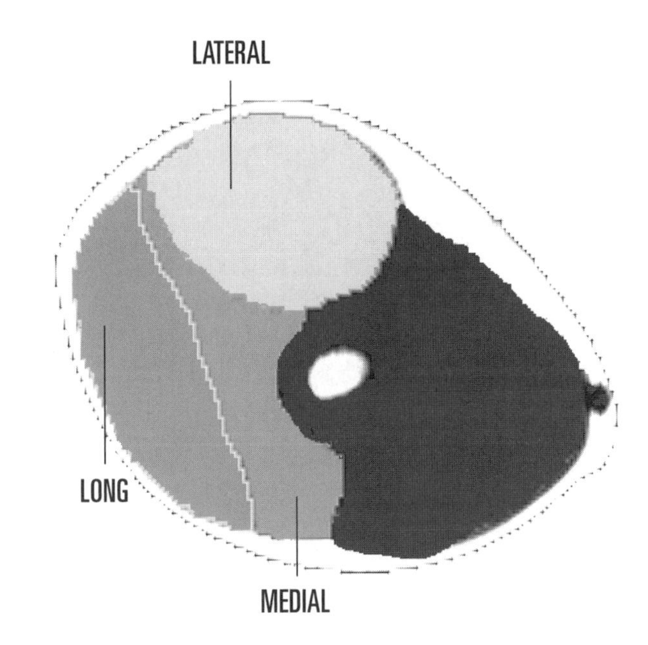

14 BENCH PRESS *with narrow grip.*

This is fairly self explanatory. The lift is done palms up, with thumbs under bar. Smoothly lower the load to the chest, pause, then smoothly raise it to the straight arm position. The idea here is not to crack the sternum, so do not bounce the weight. The elbows are held close to the body throughout the range of motion. No bridging - keep your butt on the bench.

MUSCLE FUNCTION

The MEDIAL and LATERAL HEADS of the triceps brachii are really stressed in this exercise. The long head, in contrast, seems only moderately engaged.

GUIDE

LATERAL, LONG and MEDIAL heads of triceps brachii.

The muscles of the front of the upper arm appear black because they do not contribute to the exercise. Raise your left arm up to beside of your body, palm down, and imagine looking into a slice (cross-section) of your left, upper arm.

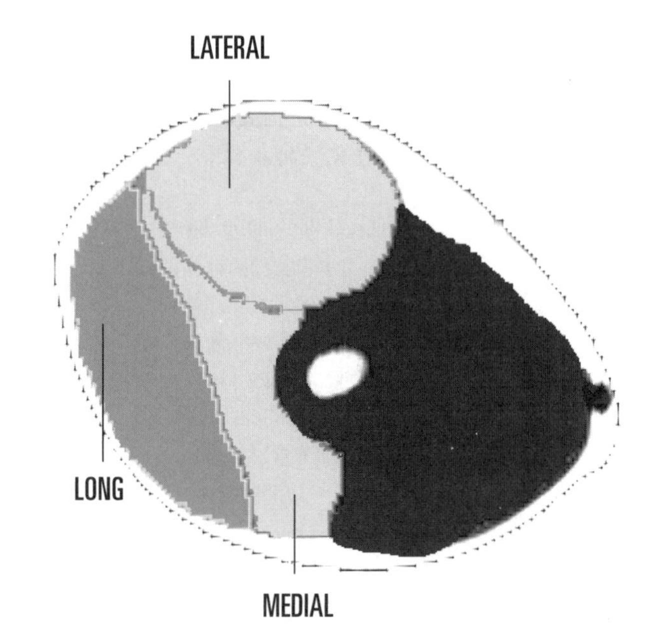

15 PARALLEL BAR DIP *with neutral grip.*

This is another classic for the triceps. Hop up in the dip bars to get started. Lower the body by somewhat relaxing. Keep the torso upright, descend as far as possible, at least until the elbows are past 90 degrees. Keep the elbows in tight. Pause at the bottom, and then push up, keeping the torso upright and the elbows in tight. Eliminate extraneous movement of the legs and head, just blast those tri's. If more stress is needed hang a few plates onto your belt.

MUSCLE FUNCTION

ALL THREE HEADS of the triceps brachii are markedly used as you raise and lower your body in this exercise that can really pump those tri's.

GUIDE

LATERAL, LONG and MEDIAL heads of triceps brachii.

The muscles of the front of the upper arm appear black because they do not contribute to the exercise. Raise your left arm up to beside of your body, palm down, and imagine looking into a slice (cross-section) of your left, upper arm.

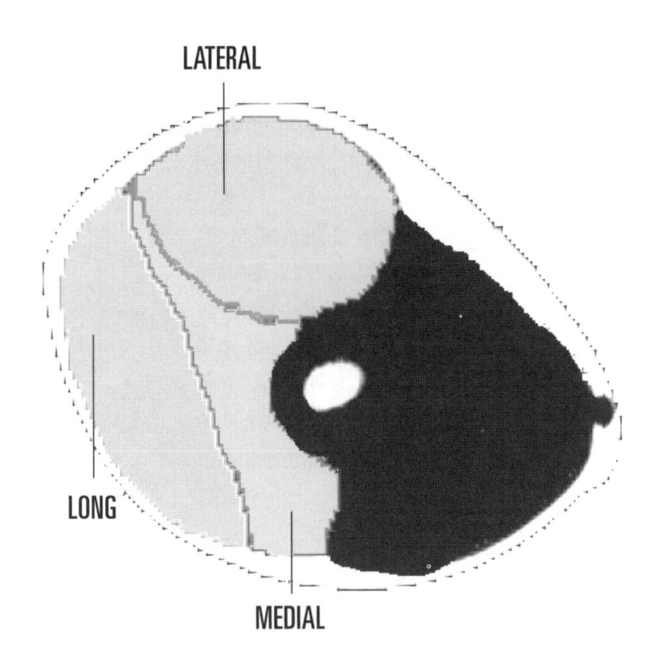

16 BENCH DIP

The most important thing is to do this exercise with a lot of control. Keep the hands pointed towards the feet, the arms straight, and then lower yourself as far as possible. After the nice smooth descent and a slight pause, mainly elbow extension is used to raise yourself to the starting position.

FINISH

START

MUSCLE FUNCTION

The fact that ALL HEADS of the triceps brachii are markedly used in this exercise should not be overly surprising because dips between benches and between parallel bars are quite similar.

GUIDE

LATERAL, LONG and MEDIAL heads of triceps brachii.

The muscles of the front of the upper arm appear black because they do not contribute to the exercise. Raise your left arm up to beside of your body, palm down, and imagine looking into a slice (cross-section) of your left, upper arm.

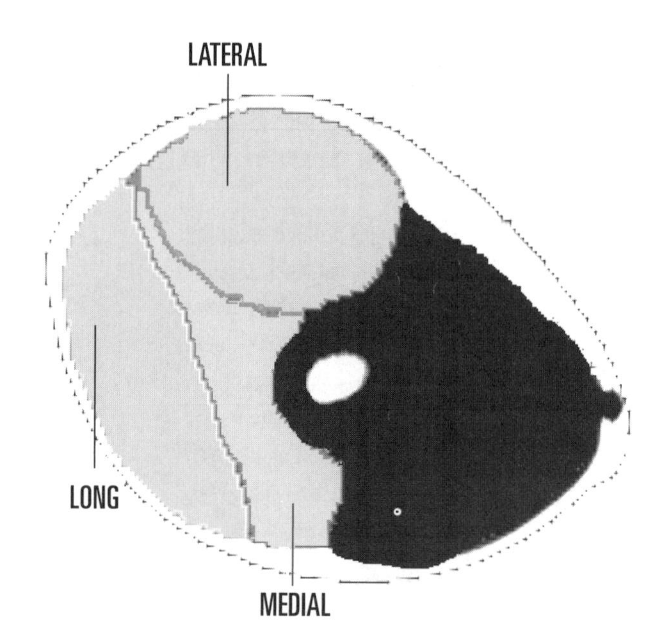

17 PULLOVER *with EZ bar and narrow grip.*

Your head should be just off the end of the bench. Begin by lowering the weight so it is held slightly off the chest (not shown). Move the bar smoothly over the head, keeping it within an inch or so of the body. Now, lower the weight as far as possible towards the floor, keeping the elbows close together. Pause at the farthest stretch, then raise the bar to just off the chest. The next rep is started by again lowering the bar over the head. Keep your butt on the bench. This is not a pressing exercise, just clear the face on the way up and down.

MUSCLE FUNCTION

The LONG HEAD showed marked use compared to its counterparts which were only slightly involved.

GUIDE

LATERAL, LONG and MEDIAL heads of triceps brachii.

The muscles of the front of the upper arm appear black because they do not contribute to the exercise. Raise your left arm up to beside of your body, palm down, and imagine looking into a slice (cross-section) of your left, upper arm.

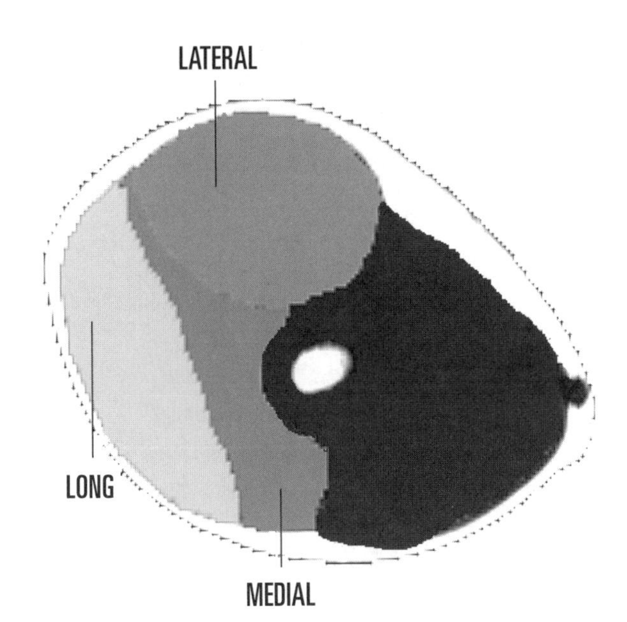

18 KICK BACK

The idea here is to really isolate the triceps. Keep the upper arm stationary, elbow tight to the body and lower the weight till the elbow angle is 90 degrees. Keeping the elbow stationary, elbow extension is done to raise the weight to the starting position.

FINISH

START

MUSCLE FUNCTION

In spite of the relatively light weight used by most of us to do this exercise, it seems to require a lot of use of the triceps brachii, especially the MEDIAL and LATERAL HEADS.

GUIDE

LATERAL, LONG and MEDIAL heads of triceps brachii.

The muscles of the front of the upper arm appear black because they do not contribute to the exercise. Raise your left arm up to beside of your body, palm down, and imagine looking into a slice (cross-section) of your left, upper arm.

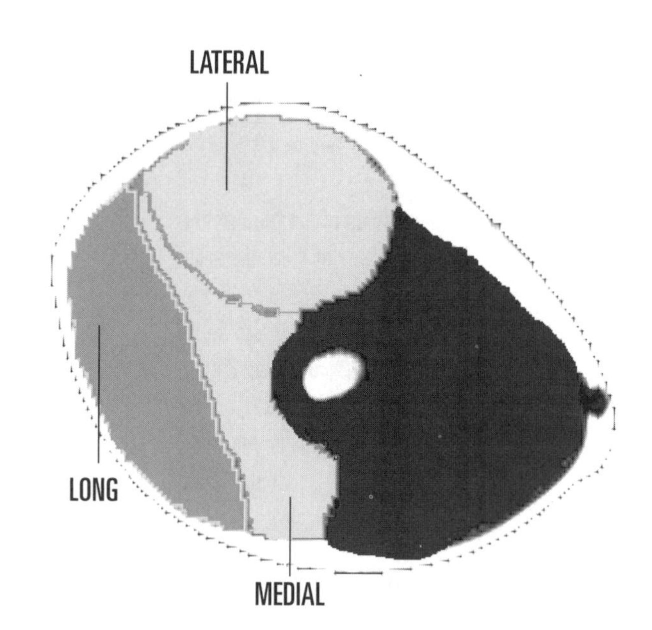

19 MILITARY PRESS *with straight bar behind neck.*

This is one of the most common exercises performed in the gym. Smoothly press the bar until the elbows are fully extended, the bar directly overhead. Pause, and then lower the weight to the starting position.

MUSCLE FUNCTION

You may be surprised by these results. The LATERAL and MEDIAL HEADS of the triceps brachii seem to be critical for getting the bar overhead in this exercise, while the long head appears to provide no assistance.

GUIDE

LATERAL, LONG and MEDIAL heads of triceps brachii.

The muscles of the front of the upper arm appear black because they do not contribute to the exercise. Raise your left arm up to beside of your body, palm down, and imagine looking into a slice (cross-section) of your left, upper arm.

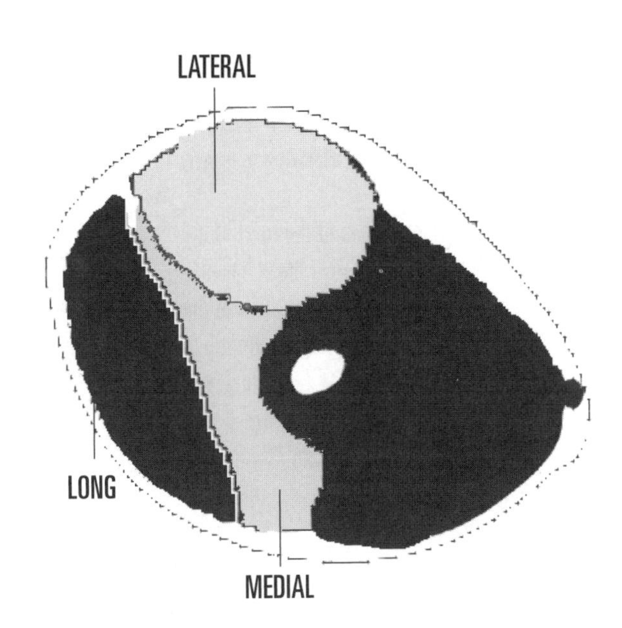

STANDING DUMBBELL PRESS *with elbows in.*

Keeping the elbows in, the dumbbells are pressed overhead. Once the elbows are extended, pause, and then smoothly lower the weight to the starting position. Try to keep elbows in front of your body to emphasize the triceps, not the shoulders.

MUSCLE FUNCTION

The pattern here is comparable to that for the military press; yet the involvement is less. The load for elbow extension is placed on the MEDIAL and LATERAL HEADS of the triceps brachii with the long head adding no help.

GUIDE

LATERAL, LONG and MEDIAL heads of triceps brachii.

The muscles of the front of the upper arm appear black because they do not contribute to the exercise. Raise your left arm up to beside of your body, palm down, and imagine looking into a slice (cross-section) of your left, upper arm.

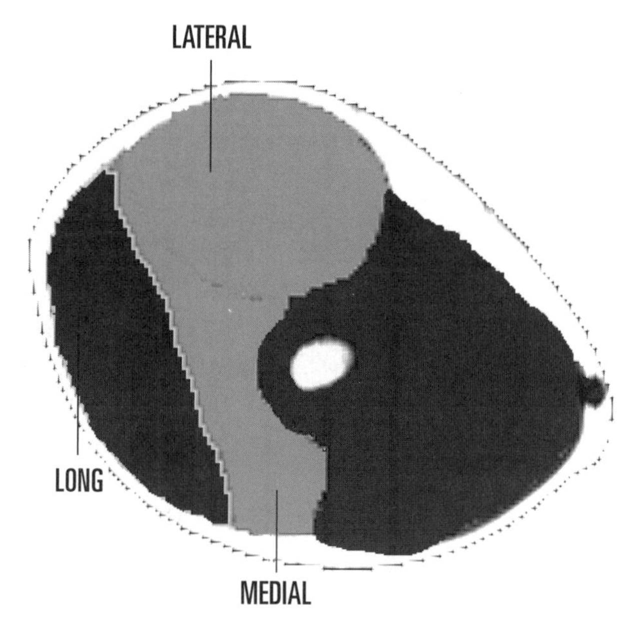

FRONT OF THE UPPER ARM

1 STANDING BICEPS CURL *with straight bar and wide grip.*

This is one of the classics, thus the execution of this exercise should be common to you. The exercise is started with the bar resting on your thighs and the torso erect. Smoothly curl the bar, raising it as far as possible, and after a slight pause, lower it to the starting position. It is crucial to keep the torso stationary. Also, keep the elbows in one place as the bar ascends and then descends.

FINISH

START

MUSCLE FUNCTION

Not surprising. All three of the major arm flexors are involved in this exercise. The brunt of the load is taken by the MEDIAL HEAD of the biceps brachii. The lateral or long head of the biceps and the brachialis make a moderate contribution to performing these curls.

GUIDE

MEDIAL (or short; next to the body) and LATERAL (or long) heads of biceps brachii and BRACHIALIS muscles.

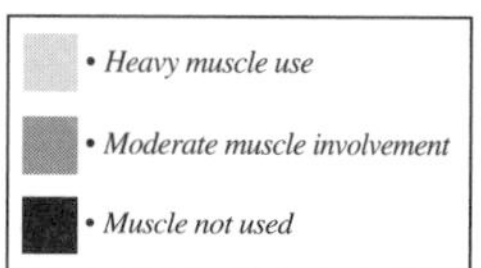

The triceps brachii muscle of the back of the upper arm appears black because it does not contribute to this exercise. Raise your left arm up to beside your body, palm down, and imagine looking into a slice (cross-section) of your left, upper arm.

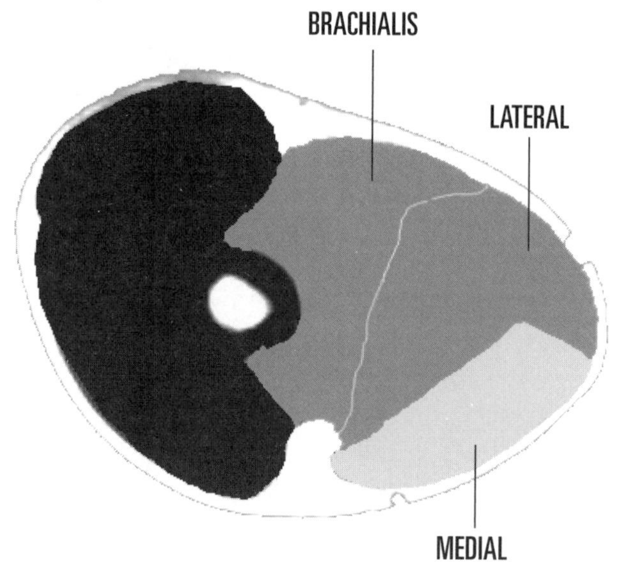

2 STANDING BICEPS CURL *with EZ bar and wide grip.*

This exercise is comparable to exercise #1, except that an EZ curl bar is used. By using the wide grip on the EZ curl bar, the hands are about shoulder width apart and the palms slightly rotated in compared to the grip that is used with the straight bar.

MUSCLE FUNCTION

The slight rotation of the hand inward to grasp the EZ bar as compared to the straight bar does not seem to alter muscle use in standing curls with a wide grip. The MEDIAL HEAD of the biceps brachii is really taxed while the lateral head and the brachialis pitch in to do some of the work.

MEDIAL (or short; next to the body) and LATERAL (or long) heads of biceps brachii and BRACHIALIS muscles.

The triceps brachii muscle of the back of the upper arm appears black because it does not contribute to this exercise. Raise your left arm up to beside your body, palm down, and imagine looking into a slice (cross-section) of your left, upper arm.

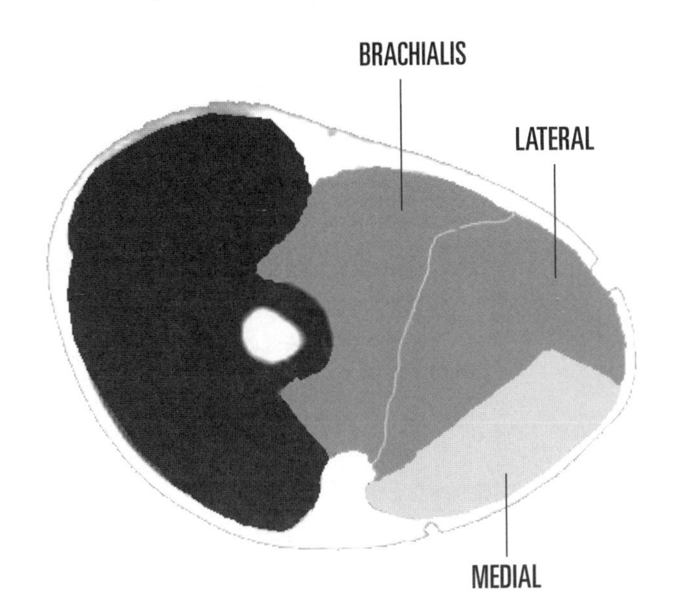

3 STANDING DUMBBELL CURL *with palms up.*

This is essentially the same exercise as #1, except that dumbbells are used instead of the straight bar. This exercise can be performed using one or two dumbbells at a time. Remember, keep the palm up, and the elbow and torso stationary.

MUSCLE FUNCTION

Standing dumbbell curls with the palm up really tax the MEDIAL HEAD of the biceps brachii with some assistance of the lateral head and the brachialis.

GUIDE

MEDIAL (or short; next to the body) and LATERAL (or long) heads of biceps brachii and BRACHIALIS muscles.

The triceps brachii muscle of the back of the upper arm appears black because it does not contribute to this exercise. Raise your left arm up to beside your body, palm down, and imagine looking into a slice (cross-section) of your left, upper arm.

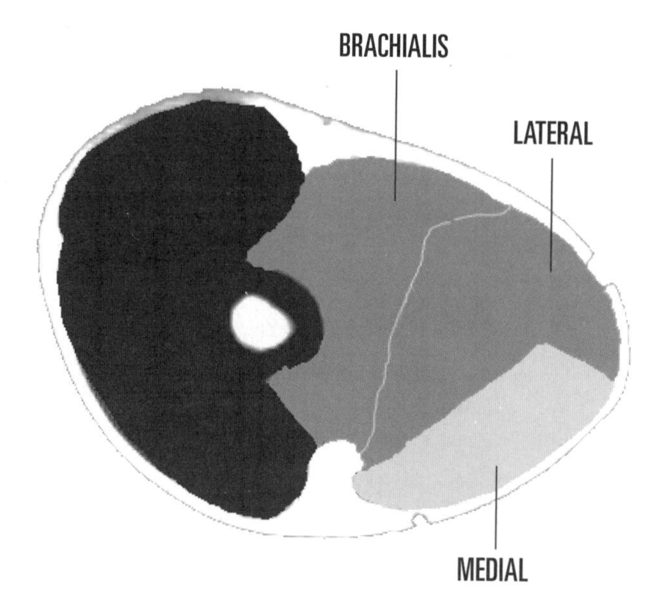

STANDING DUMBBELL CURL *with neutral grip.*

This is just like the aforementioned exercise (#3) except for the grip. In the neutral position, the dumbbells are held such that the palms face the body throughout the range of motion.

MUSCLE FUNCTION

Things are starting to be different now. The LATERAL HEAD does the brunt of the work. The medial head and the brachialis are only moderately involved.

GUIDE

MEDIAL (or short; next to the body) and LATERAL (or long) heads of biceps brachii and BRACHIALIS muscles.

The triceps brachii muscle of the back of the upper arm appears black because it does not contribute to this exercise. Raise your left arm up to beside your body, palm down, and imagine looking into a slice (cross-section) of your left, upper arm.

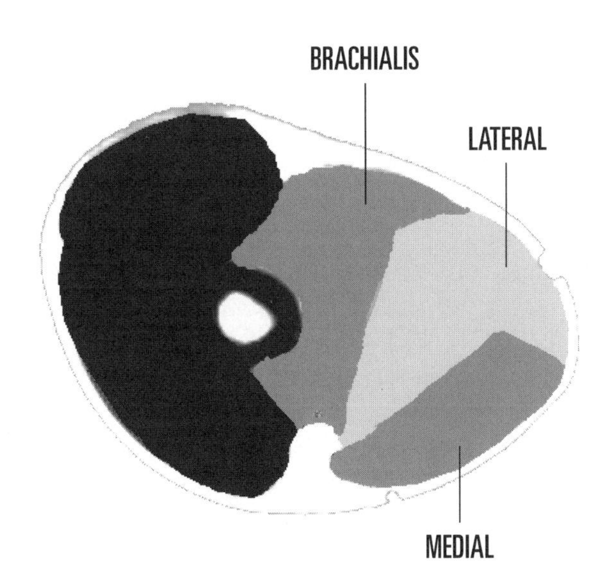

5 STANDING DUMBBELL CURL *with lateral rotation.*

This exercise is a combination of #3 and #4. It starts with dumbbells held in the neutral position. As the weight is raised, however, the palms are rotated out such that at the end of the range of motion, the thumbs point away from body.

GUIDE

MEDIAL (or short; next to the body) and LATERAL (or long) heads of biceps brachii and BRACHIALIS muscles.

The triceps brachii muscle of the back of the upper arm appears black because it does not contribute to this exercise. Raise your left arm up to beside your body, palm down, and imagine looking into a slice (cross-section) of your left, upper arm.

MUSCLE FUNCTION

So what would be expected if you did curls by starting in the neutral position and rotated the palms up as you raised the load. BOTH HEADS of the biceps brachii enjoy severe stress. This is not the case for the brachialis, which again shows moderate use.

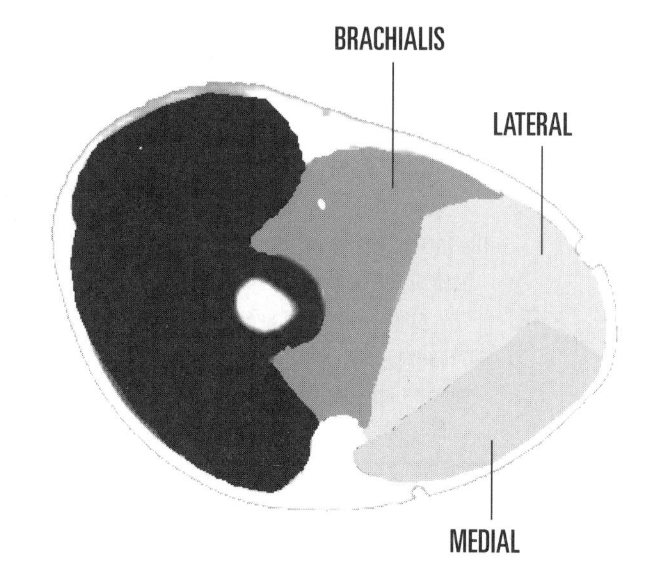

6 INCLINE SEATED DUMBBELL CURL *with lateral rotation.*

This exercise is executed just like #5 (standing dumbbell curl with lateral rotation), except you are sitting on an incline bench. Remember, keep your upper body stationary and feel that stretch.

MUSCLE FUNCTION

This exercise stresses BOTH HEADS of the biceps brachii with less support from the brachialis.

GUIDE

MEDIAL (or short; next to the body) and LATERAL (or long) heads of biceps brachii and BRACHIALIS muscles.

The triceps brachii muscle of the back of the upper arm appears black because it does not contribute to this exercise. Raise your left arm up to beside your body, palm down, and imagine looking into a slice (cross-section) of your left, upper arm

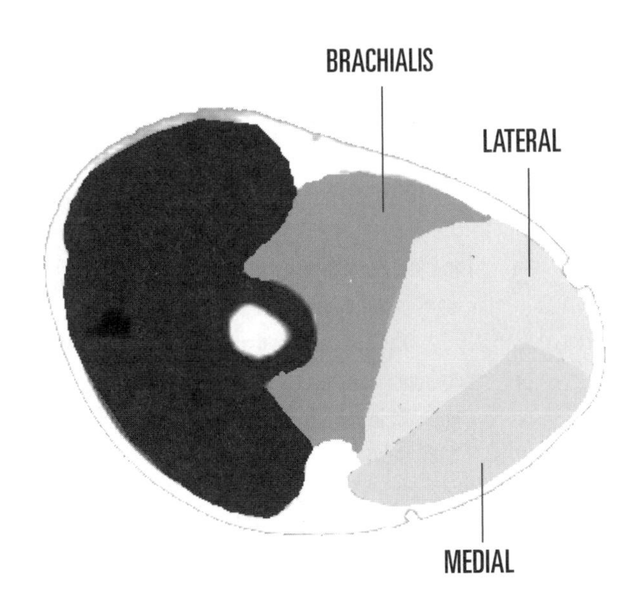

7 INCLINE SEATED DUMBBELL CURL *with neutral grip.*

This exercise is just like #6 except that the hands remain in the neutral position (palms facing body) throughout the range of motion.

FINISH

START

MUSCLE FUNCTION

By keeping a neutral grip throughout the range of motion, the LATERAL HEAD of the biceps brachii and the BRACHIALIS are really stressed. The medial head is only moderately involved.

GUIDE

MEDIAL (or short; next to the body) and LATERAL (or long) heads of biceps brachii and BRACHIALIS muscles.

The triceps brachii muscle of the back of the upper arm appears black because it does not contribute to this exercise. Raise your left arm up to beside your body, palm down, and imagine looking into a slice (cross-section) of your left, upper arm.

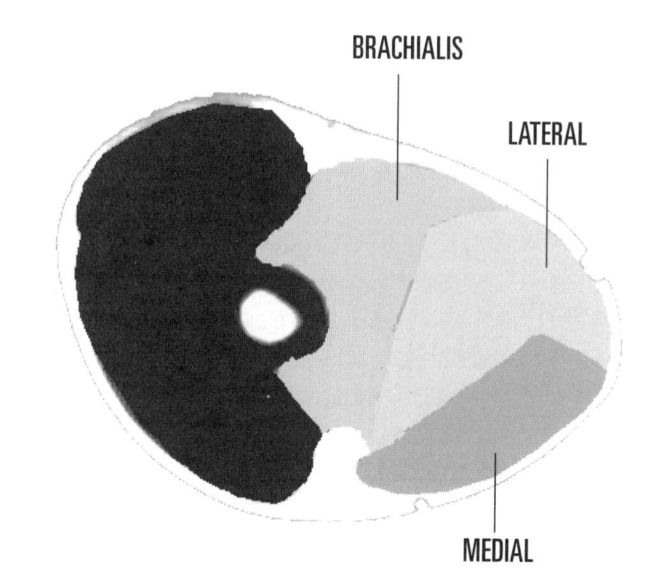

8 INCLINE SEATED DUMBBELL CURL *with palm up.*

This exercise is just like #7 except that the hands are held palm up throughout the range of motion.

MUSCLE FUNCTION

By using the palm up position throughout the range of motion, BOTH HEADS of the biceps brachii are maximally stressed. The brachialis shows less involvement.

GUIDE

MEDIAL (or short; next to the body) and LATERAL (or long) heads of biceps brachii and BRACHIALIS muscles.

The triceps brachii muscle of the back of the upper arm appears black because it does not contribute to this exercise. Raise your left arm up to beside your body, palm down, and imagine looking into a slice (cross-section) of your left, upper arm.

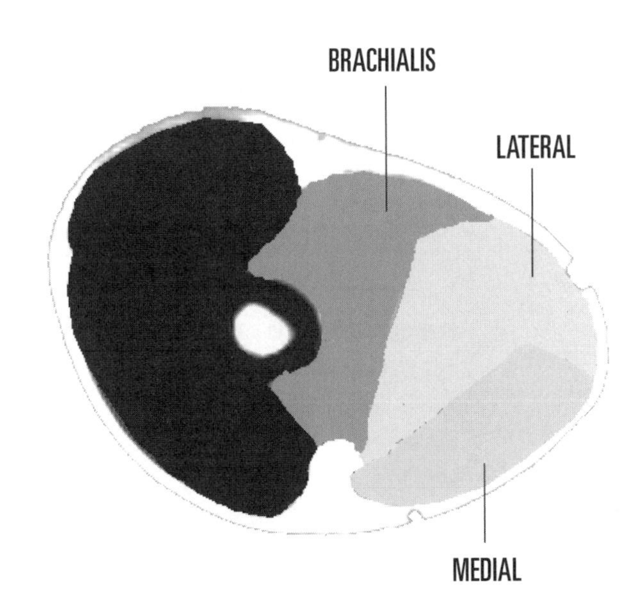

9 STANDING BICEPS CURL *with EZ bar and arm blaster.*

This exercise is just like exercise #2, except it is done using an arm blaster. This really isolates the biceps. You can get similar isolation by bracing your arm(s) against an incline bench ("Preacher curl"). Be careful when lowering the weight, the excellent isolation can lead one to hyperextend the elbows at the bottom of descent of the bar.

MUSCLE FUNCTION

The MEDIAl and LATERAL HEADS of the biceps brachii get busted good. The brachialis is involved somewhat less.

GUIDE

MEDIAL (or short; next to the body) and LATERAL (or long) heads of biceps brachii and BRACHIALIS muscles.

The triceps brachii muscle of the back of the upper arm appears black because it does not contribute to this exercise. Raise your left arm up to beside your body, palm down, and imagine looking into a slice (cross-section) of your left, upper arm.

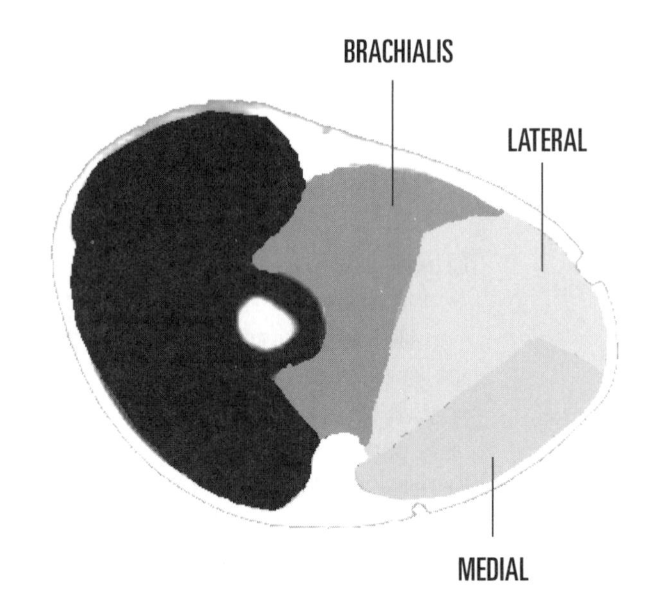

10 STANDING BICEPS CURL *with straight bar and arm blaster.*

This is just like exercise #9 except a straight bar is used. Again, you can use an incline bench instead of an arm blaster to isolate the biceps.

MUSCLE FUNCTION

All THREE MUSCLES in the FRONT of those big guns get a chance to enjoy the utmost training stimulus if one will just do It.

GUIDE

MEDIAL (or short; next to the body) and LATERAL (or long) heads of biceps brachii and BRACHIALIS muscles.

The triceps brachii muscle of the back of the upper arm appears black because it does not contribute to this exercise. Raise your left arm up to beside your body, palm down, and imagine looking into a slice (cross-section) of your left, upper arm.

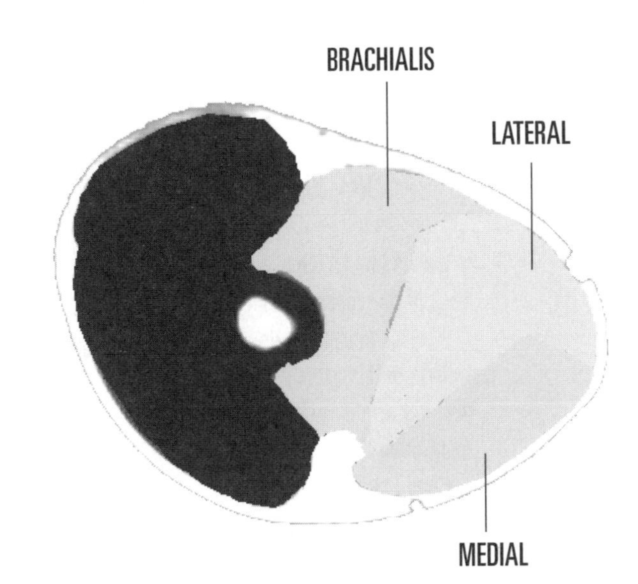

11 STANDING BICEPS CURL *with straight bar and narrow grip.*

This is like exercise #1 for the front of the upper arm, except a narrow grip is used.

MUSCLE FUNCTION

Here, ALL THREE major elbow flexors get to enjoy a marked training stimulus. As compared to the wide grip version of this exercise, the narrow grip seems a more natural movement which allows one to more completely isolate the elbow flexors and eliminate extraneous movement. As with exercise #10, this seems to really blast the front of the upper arms.

MEDIAL (or short; next to the body) and LATERAL (or long) heads of biceps brachii and BRACHIALIS muscles.

The triceps brachii muscle of the back of the upper arm appears black because it does not contribute to this exercise. Raise your left arm up to beside your body, palm down, and imagine looking into a slice (cross-section) of your left, upper arm.

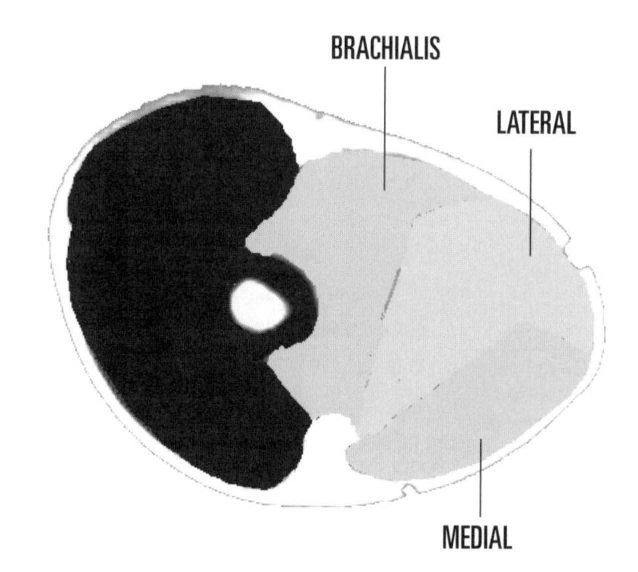

THIGH

1 LUNGE

This exercise takes coordination to perform, and most people have a tendency to do it incorrectly. The idea is to keep the torso erect. Step forward with the left leg 2 to 3 feet, allowing the body to descend towards the floor in a controlled fashion. Stop the descent when the knee of the right leg is about to touch the floor. At this time the left knee should be flexed a little past 90 degrees. Now, using the left leg, drive up and step back to the starting position. You can alternate legs, or do unilateral lunges. Alternatively, instead of a bar, you can use a pair of dumbbells to perform this exercise.

MUSCLE FUNCTION

This exercise really hits the ADDUCTOR MAGNUS (AD M) and BREVIS (AD B) of the forward leg. It also involves the three vasti muscles (VL, VM and VI), but moderately.

GUIDE

AD B=Adductor brevis
AD L=Adductor longus
AD M=Adductor magnus
BF=Biceps femoris
GR=Gracilis
RF=Rectus femoris
SR=Sartorius
ST=Semitendinosus
VM=Vastus medialis
VL=Vastus lateralis
VI=Vastus intermedius

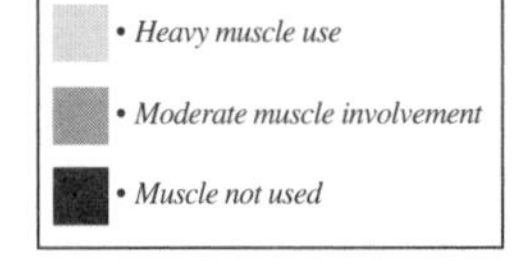

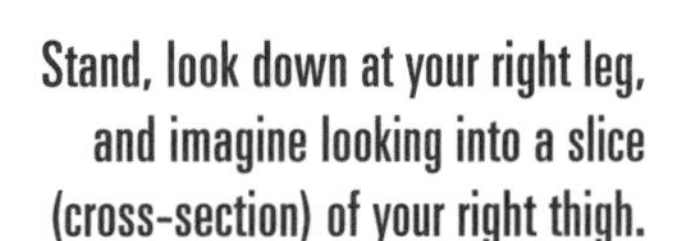

Stand, look down at your right leg, and imagine looking into a slice (cross-section) of your right thigh.

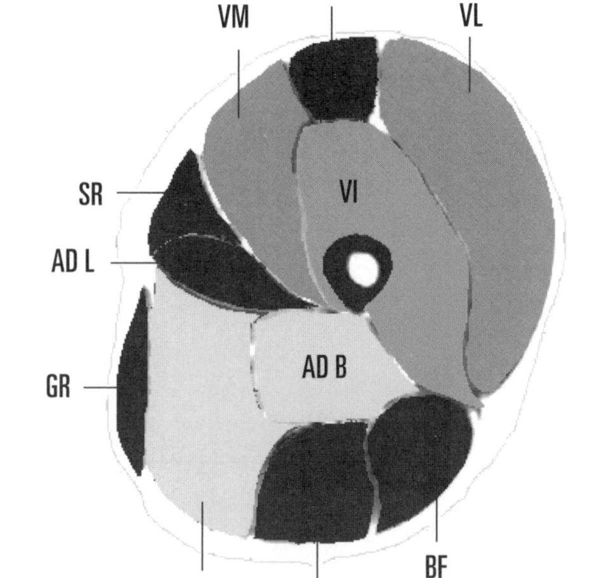

2 SEATED KNEE EXTENSION

The way to do this activity is self explanatory. Unilateral or bilateral exercise can be done. Smoothly, raise the weight by contracting the thighs until the legs are completely extended, and after a slight pause lower the load to the starting position. No cheating, keep your butt on the seat and sit still throughout the full range of motion.

MUSCLE FUNCTION

This exercise activates ALL FOUR MUSCLES of the QUADRICEPS FEMORIS (VI, VM, VL and RF) maximally. With the feet in a neutral position, the four muscles share the load equally.

GUIDE

AD B=Adductor brevis
AD L=Adductor longus
AD M=Adductor magnus
BF=Biceps femoris
GR=Gracilis
RF=Rectus femoris
SR=Sartorius
ST=Semitendinosus
VM=Vastus medialis
VL=Vastus lateralis
VI=Vastus intermedius

Stand, look down at your right leg, and imagine looking into a slice (cross-section) of your right thigh.

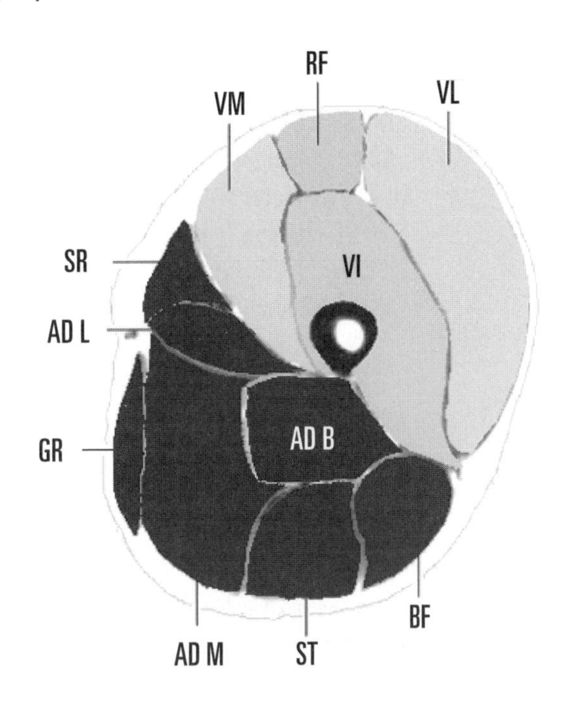

3 SEATED KNEE EXTENSION *with toes in.*

This exercise is just like the previous seated knee extensions (#2) except that the feet are rotated inward as far as possible throughout the full range of motion.

MUSCLE FUNCTION

By rotating the feet inward, the rectus femoris (RF) and the vastus medialis(VM) show only moderate involvement while the VASTUS LATERALIS (VL) and VASTUS INTERMEDIUS (VI) are maximally stressed

GUIDE

AD B=Adductor brevis
AD L=Adductor longus
AD M=Adductor magnus
BF=Biceps femoris
GR=Gracilis
RF=Rectus femoris
SR=Sartorius
ST=Semitendinosus
VM=Vastus medialis
VL=Vastus lateralis
VI=Vastus intermedius

Stand, look down at your right leg, and imagine looking into a slice (cross-section) of your right thigh.

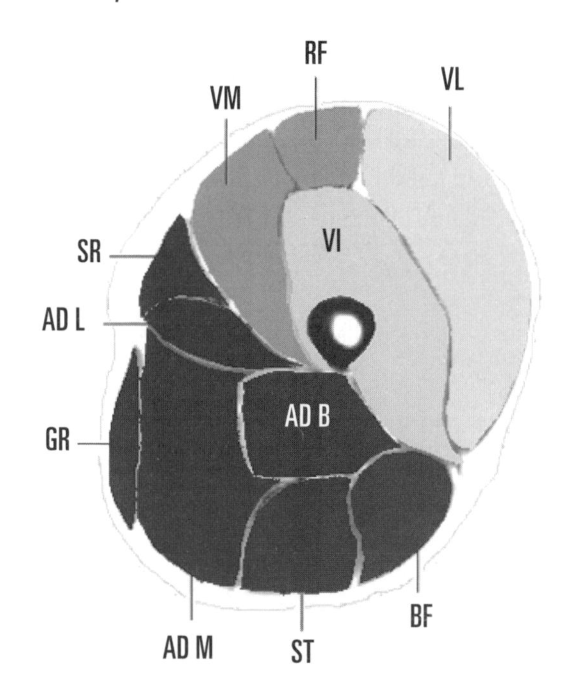

MRI

4 SEATED KNEE EXTENSION *with toes out.*

This is just like the two previous seated knee extension exercises (#2, 3) except the feet are rotated laterally as far as possible throughout the full range of motion.

MUSCLE FUNCTION

Rotation of the feet outward reduces involvement of the vastus lateralis (VL). The VASTUS MEDIALIS (VM), VASTUS INTERMEDIUS (VM) and RECTUS FEMORIS (RF) show maximal involvement

GUIDE

AD B=Adductor brevis
AD L=Adductor longus
AD M=Adductor magnus
BF=Biceps femoris
GR=Gracilis
RF=Rectus femoris
SR=Sartorius
ST=Semitendinosus
VM=Vastus medialis
VL=Vastus lateralis
VI=Vastus intermedius

Stand, look down at your right leg, and imagine looking into a slice (cross-section) of your right thigh.

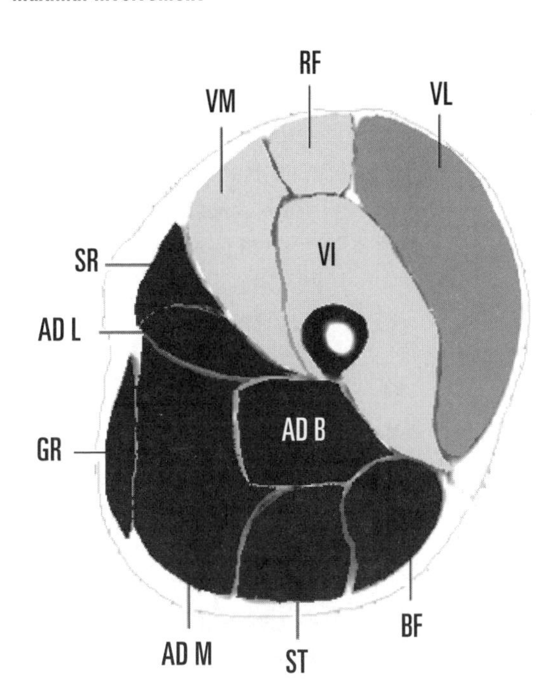

5 BACK SQUAT *with narrow stance.*

Now we get down to some real exercise. Turn those legs to jelly, squat till you drop. Descend by driving the knees forward out over the toes and dropping the rump slightly behind the heels. Keep that back upright with a slight arch. Stop the descent when the thighs are about parallel to the floor. Now, keeping the torso upright, raise the bar in exactly the reverse motion of how it was lowered. Do not descend too fast, as stopping the bar at the bottom and raising it may require excessive forward lean. Remain upright to emphasize use of the thighs.

MUSCLE FUNCTION

This exercise stresses the THREE VASTI MUSCLES (VL, VI and VM). The rectus femoris (RF), like the three adductor muscles (AD M, AD B and AD L), shows moderate involvement. This is a good example illustrating that even some of the toughest quad exercises do not automatically stress all four heads.

GUIDE

AD B=Adductor brevis
AD L=Adductor longus
AD M=Adductor magnus
BF=Biceps femoris
GR=Gracilis
RF=Rectus femoris
SR=Sartorius
ST=Semitendinosus
VM=Vastus medialis
VL=Vastus lateralis
VI=Vastus intermedius

Stand, look down at your right leg, and imagine looking into a slice (cross-section) of your right thigh.

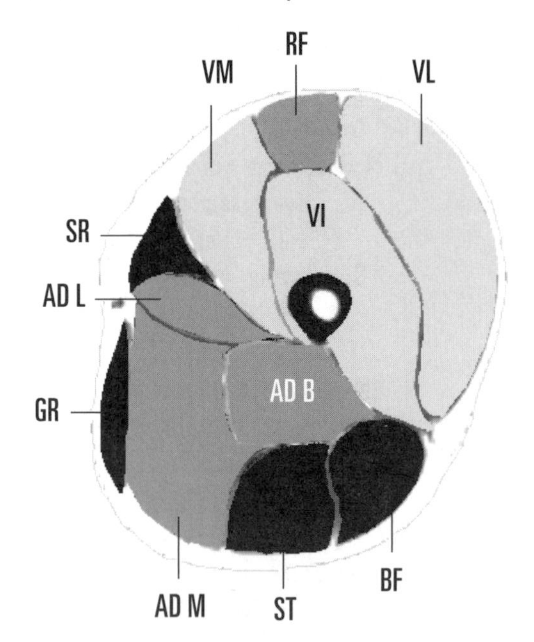

6 CLASSICAL BACK SQUAT

This is just like the narrow stance squat (#5) except for position of the feet. This exercise should be done with toes pointed straight ahead or slightly out and the feet about shoulder width apart. So, just hang some plates and do it.

MUSCLE FUNCTION

This exercise involves the THREE VASTI MUSCLES (VL, VM and VI) most heavily. The rectus femoris (RF) and the three adductor muscles (AD M, AD L and AD B) show moderate use. Why can you do more weight with this exercise? With this classical squat, as compared to the narrow stance squat, use of the powerful glutes and back muscles is probably greater. For isolation of the quads and additional use of the adductors the narrow stance may be preferable.

GUIDE

AD B=Adductor brevis
AD L=Adductor longus
AD M=Adductor magnus
BF=Biceps femoris
GR=Gracilis
RF=Rectus femoris
SR=Sartorius
ST=Semitendinosus
VM=Vastus medialis
VL=Vastus lateralis
VI=Vastus intermedius

Stand, look down at your right leg, and imagine looking into a slice (cross-section) of your right thigh.

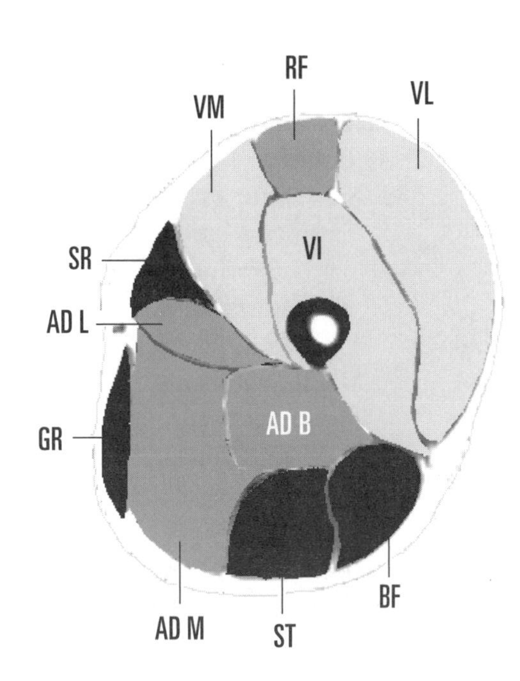

7 FRONT SQUAT

This exercise is just like the classical squat (#6) except you are now holding the bar in front of your body. Place feet about shoulder width apart with the toes pointed ahead or slightly out. Lower yourself nice and slow until the thighs are parallel to the floor. Remember, keep your head up and back straight. Make a distinct stop and then push back up with good form.

START

FINISH

MUSCLE FUNCTION

The front squat with barbell requires the same muscle use as the two previous back squat exercises (#5, 6). The THREE HEADS of the VASTI MUSCLE (VL, VI and VM) are heavily used. The rectus femoris (RF) and the three adductor muscles (AD B, AD M and AD B) show moderate stress.

GUIDE

AD B=Adductor brevis
AD L=Adductor longus
AD M=Adductor magnus
BF=Biceps femoris
GR=Gracilis
RF=Rectus femoris
SR=Sartorius
ST=Semitendinosus
VM=Vastus medialis
VL=Vastus lateralis
VI=Vastus intermedius

Stand, look down at your right leg, and imagine looking into a slice (cross-section) of your right thigh.

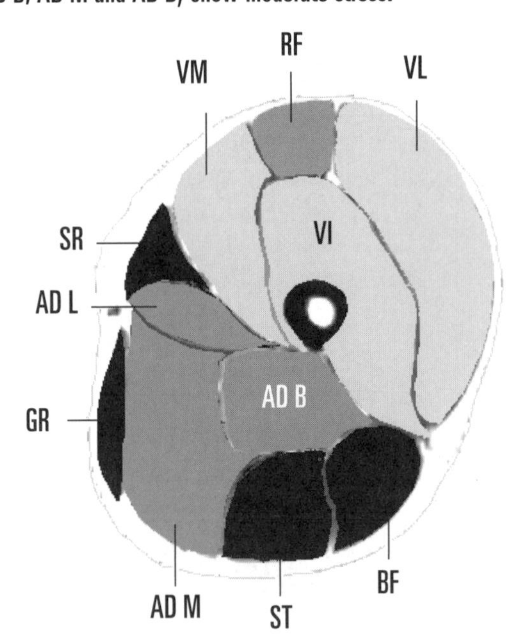

8 FRONT SQUAT *in Smith rack.*

This is just like the previous exercise (#7) except it is done in a Smith rack. Remember to keep the torso as erect as possible during this or any other squat. Squatting in front of a mirror always helps to maintain good form.

MUSCLE FUNCTION

This exercise targets the THREE VASTI MUSCLES (VL, VM and VI). The adductor magnus (AD M) and longus (AD L) are not used. There is moderate use of the rectus femoris (RF), sartorius (SR), semitendinosus (ST), adductor brevis (AD B) and biceps femoris (BF). This different pattern of muscle use from front squats may stem from the fact that the Smith machine makes it easier to maintain vertical movement.

GUIDE

AD B=Adductor brevis
AD L=Adductor longus
AD M=Adductor magnus
BF=Biceps femoris
GR=Gracilis
RF=Rectus femoris
SR=Sartorius
ST=Semitendinosus
VM=Vastus medialis
VL=Vastus lateralis
VI=Vastus intermedius

Stand, look down at your right leg, and imagine looking into a slice (cross-section) of your right thigh.

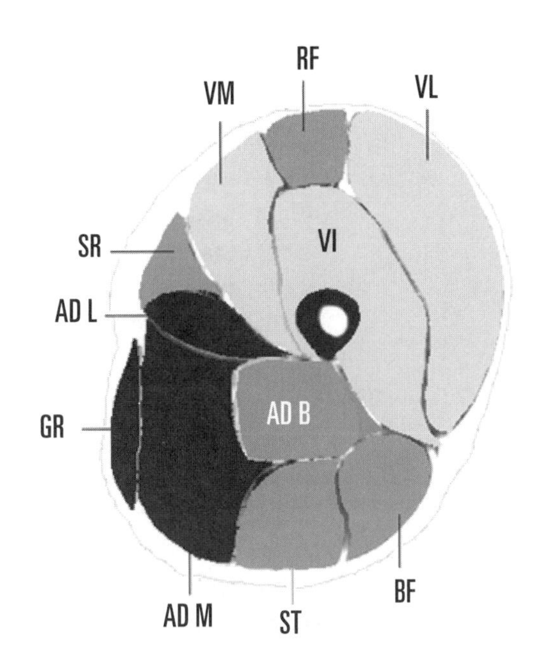

9 HACK SQUAT *with feet in front of body.*

So, now you really want to isolate those quads. Hack squats are very comparable to free weight squats except for a few important items. In the hack squat, done in a machine, you do not have to balance a bar; just push against the resistance through your shoulders. Also the feet are placed on a special platform. This gives one the opportunity to place the base of support, your feet, directly under the hips, or as done in this version of the hack squat, out in front of the body. Hack squats also allow for a more complete range of motion as descent is usually not stopped until the knee joint is flexed well beyond 90 degrees. Finally, the load is placed upon the body by slightly extending at the hip and knee joints (this raises the sledge) and moving the mechanical stops such that you can lower the weight.

Good luck, and just bust some reps!

MUSCLE FUNCTION

This exercise involves some muscles that we have not seen activated in previous squat exercises. The VASTUS LATERALIS (VL) and INTERMEDIUS (VI) do the majority of the work. The large ADDUCTOR MAGNUS (AD M) and BREVIS (AD B) show as much use. The vastus medialis (VM), gracilis (GR) and sartorius (SR) muscles are moderately used. The rectus femoris (RF) is not used.

GUIDE

AD B=Adductor brevis
AD L=Adductor longus
AD M=Adductor magnus
BF=Biceps femoris
GR=Gracilis
RF=Rectus femoris
SR=Sartorius
ST=Semitendinosus
VM=Vastus medialis
VL=Vastus lateralis
VI=Vastus intermedius

Stand, look down at your right leg, and imagine looking into a slice (cross-section) of your right thigh.

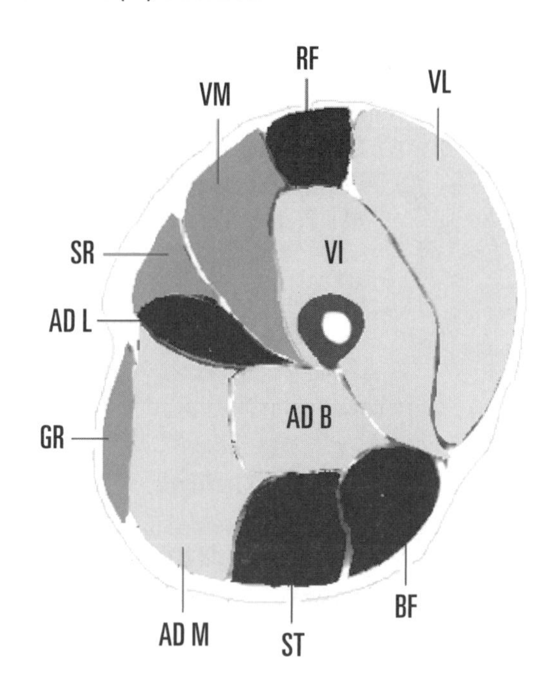

10 HACK SQUAT *with feet under hips.*

This exercise is just like #9 except the feet are placed directly under the hips.

MUSCLE FUNCTION

Placing the feet under the hips evokes even greater muscle use than the previous hack squat exercise. The VASTUS LATERALIS (VL) and INTERMEDIUS (VI) and the ADDUCTOR MAGNUS (AD M) and BREVIS (AD B) muscles as well as the GRACILIS (GR) show maximal stress. The rectus femoris, vastus medialis, sartorius and adductor longus are also quite involved.

GUIDE

AD B=Adductor brevis
AD L=Adductor longus
AD M=Adductor magnus
BF=Biceps femoris
GR=Gracilis
RF=Rectus femoris
SR=Sartorius
ST=Semitendinosus
VM=Vastus medialis
VL=Vastus lateralis
VI=Vastus intermedius

Stand, look down at your right leg, and imagine looking into a slice (cross-section) of your right thigh.

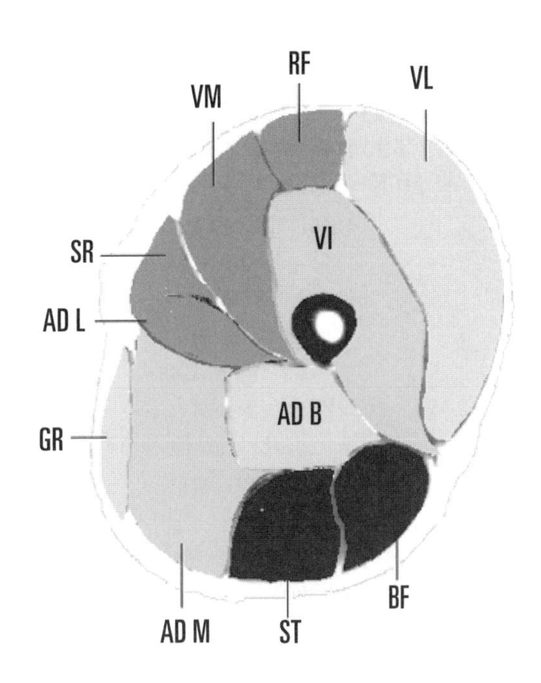

THIGH

11 OLD STYLE HACK SQUAT

Before the hack squat machine came around, bodybuilders used to perform this exercise with a barbell. Sometimes it is incorrectly referred to as Sissy squat. A bar is held behind the body to add extra resistance. Stand in front of an Olympic bar, bend over and grasp it with both hands (reverse grip with one or both hands). While keeping the back straight and extended as far as possible, do a partial toe raise such that the heels are off the floor. Now, extend at the hip and knee joints to the erect position. Pause after completely extending, and then lower the bar to the floor while keeping up on the toes and the back upright. Oh, what a burn!

MUSCLE FUNCTION

Muscle use for this exercise is similar to that for the Sissy squat (#12). THE ENTIRE QUADRICEPS FEMORIS (VL, VM, VI and RF) is "lit up". The adductor magnus (AD M) is used moderately. Although it takes a few sessions to learn how to do this exercise, it is rewarding because of its great effect on the quad.

GUIDE

AD B=Adductor brevis
AD L=Adductor longus
AD M=Adductor magnus
BF=Biceps femoris
GR=Gracilis
RF=Rectus femoris
SR=Sartorius
ST=Semitendinosus
VM=Vastus medialis
VL=Vastus lateralis
VI=Vastus intermedius

Stand, look down at your right leg, and imagine looking into a slice (cross-section) of your right thigh.

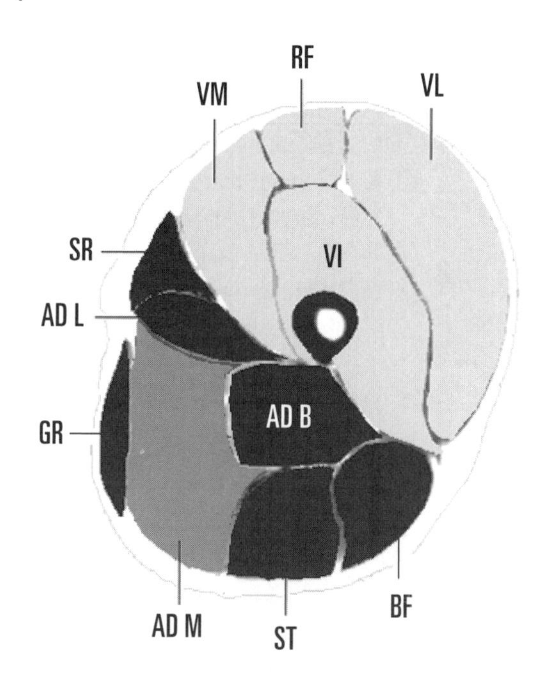

12 SISSY SQUAT

The name belies the difficulty of this exercise. Stand beside a solid support and grasp it with one hand. Now, execute a toe raise, get those heels up off the floor. OK, you are ready to get serious. Descend by forcing the knees way out over the toes, and leaning slightly back. Descend as far as possible, maybe until the thigh rests on the leg. After a short pause, get those quads going and return to the starting position. During ascent, remain up on the toes, and keep the torso leaning slightly back. Once you get this down, resistance can be added by holding a plate across the chest/abdomen with the opposite arm. Do not use the supporting arm, which is for balance, to help in pulling you up.

FINISH

START

MUSCLE FUNCTION

All four muscles (VL, VM, VI and RF) of the QUADRICEPS FEMORIS show full involvement. The three vasti muscles are very active in all kinds of squats. The rectus femoris is not. In contrast to the vasti muscles, it crosses two joints and is sometimes used to perform flexion at the hip. To bring it into action you must pick exercises where the hip is rather fixed - like this one!

GUIDE

AD B=Adductor brevis
AD L=Adductor longus
AD M=Adductor magnus
BF=Biceps femoris
GR=Gracilis
RF=Rectus femoris
SR=Sartorius
ST=Semitendinosus
VM=Vastus medialis
VL=Vastus lateralis
VI=Vastus intermedius

Stand, look down at your right leg, and imagine looking into a slice (cross-section) of your right thigh.

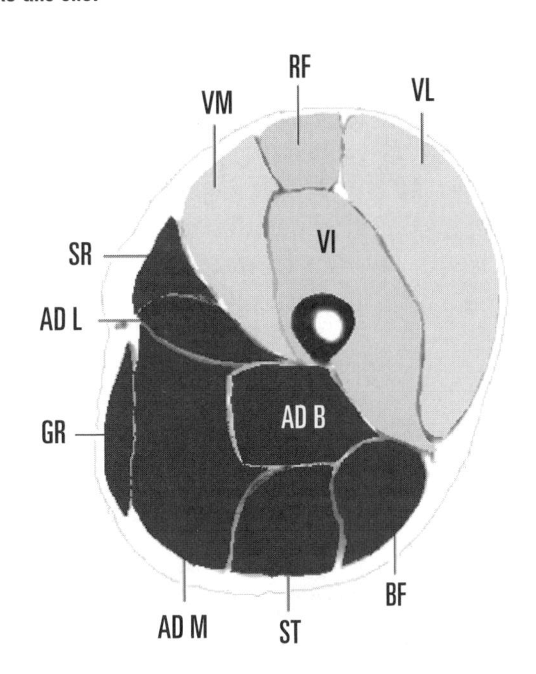

13 LEG PRESS *with feet high.*

In this version of the leg press, the feet are placed high on the platform about shoulder width apart. As with the hack squat, you have to slightly extend at the hip and knee joints and move the mechanical stops with your hands so you can lower the weight. Let the load descend until the knee joints are at least at 90 degrees, and after a short pause, use those tree stumps to push the sledge to the starting position.

MUSCLE FUNCTION

As expected, this is a great exercise for thigh development. It really hits the THREE VASTI MUSCLES (VL, VI and VM) and the ADDUCTOR MAGNUS(AD M) and BREVIS (AD B). There is moderate use of the adductor longus (AD L). It leaves the rectus femoris (RF) unused, probably because of the large hip flexion.

GUIDE

AD B=Adductor brevis
AD L=Adductor longus
AD M=Adductor magnus
BF=Biceps femoris
GR=Gracilis
RF=Rectus femoris
SR=Sartorius
ST=Semitendinosus
VM=Vastus medialis
VL=Vastus lateralis
VI=Vastus intermedius

Stand, look down at your right leg, and imagine looking into a slice (cross-section) of your right thigh.

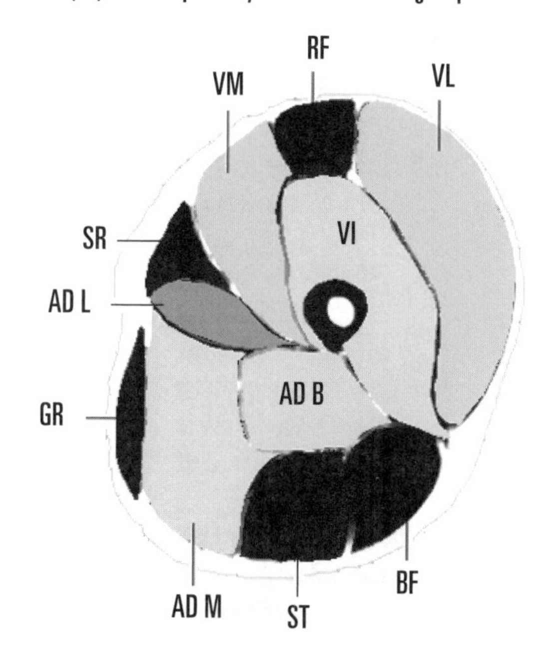

14 LEG PRESS *with feet low.*

This exercise is just like #13 except that the feet are placed low on the platform, as far as possible under the hips.

MUSCLE FUNCTION

Moving the feet down on the platform when you do the leg press, evokes greater knee joint flexion. Again, the THREE VASTI MUSCLES (VL, VI and VM) and the ADDUCTOR MAGNUS (AD M) and BREVIS (AD B) show marked use. The differences are that the adductor longus (AD L) is not used and the biceps femoris (BF) is somewhat brought into play.

GUIDE

AD B=Adductor brevis
AD L=Adductor longus
AD M=Adductor magnus
BF=Biceps femoris
GR=Gracilis
RF=Rectus femoris
SR=Sartorius
ST=Semitendinosus
VM=Vastus medialis
VL=Vastus lateralis
VI=Vastus intermedius

Stand, look down at your right leg, and imagine looking into a slice (cross-section) of your right thigh.

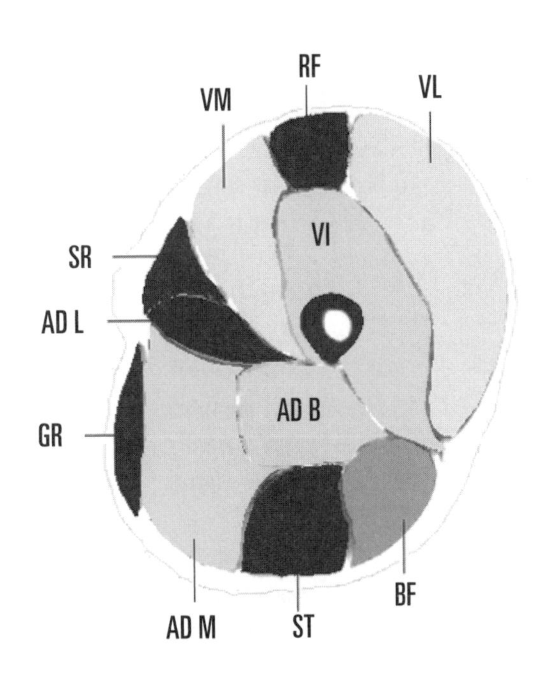

15 STIFF LEGGED DEADLIFT

This is like the classic deadlift almost everyone can envision with some major exceptions. Stand on a box or the end of a stable bench directly behind the bar with the feet somewhat less than shoulder width apart. Bend over at the waist, keep those knees straight, and grasp the bar with one or both hands reversed. The bar is raised in a smooth fashion using the hip and back extensors until the torso is erect. After a slight pause, lower the bar toward the feet, really emphasizing a large range of motion and getting a good stretch. Again, keep those knees rather straight.

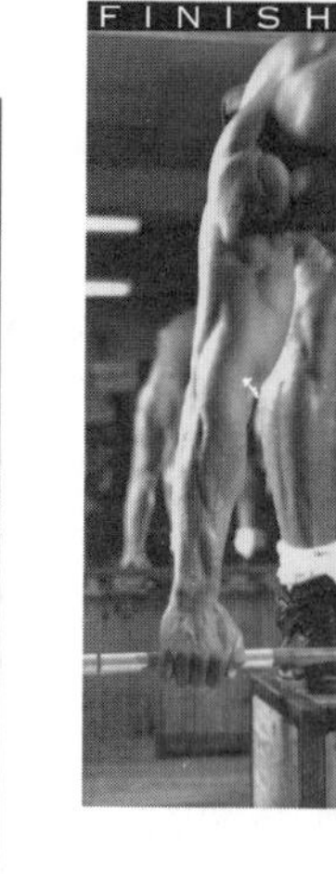

MUSCLE FUNCTION

The stiff legged deadlift uses most of the rear muscles of the thigh. The adductor magnus (AD M) and brevis (AD B), biceps femoris (BF) and semitendinosus (ST) show moderate use.

GUIDE

AD B=Adductor brevis
AD L=Adductor longus
AD M=Adductor magnus
BF=Biceps femoris
GR=Gracilis
RF=Rectus femoris
SR=Sartorius
ST=Semitendinosus
VM=Vastus medialis
VL=Vastus lateralis
VI=Vastus intermedius

Stand, look down at your right leg, and imagine looking into a slice (cross-section) of your right thigh.

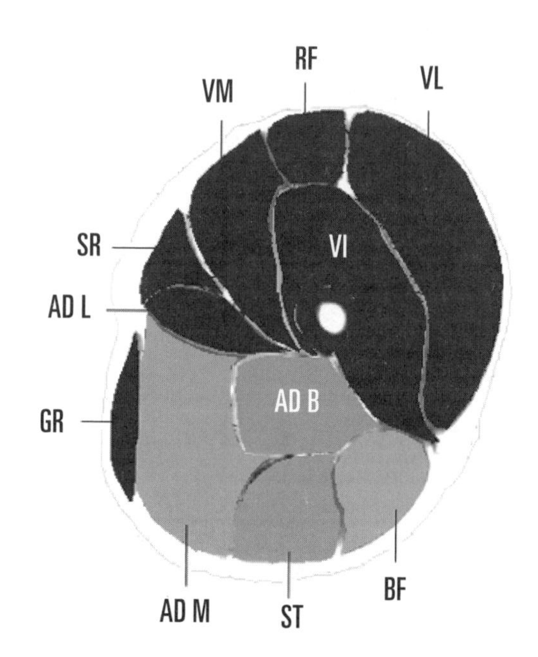

16 STIFF LEGGED DEADLIFT *with elevation.*

This is just like the aforementioned exercise (#15), except that the balls of the feet are elevated 1 to 2 inches on a stable object. This adds more stretch to the calves and back of the thighs.

MUSCLE FUNCTION

This exercise moderately works the adductor magnus (AD M) and brevis (AD B) and the biceps femoris (BF). Elevation of the balls of the feet did not increase involvement of the hamstring muscles.

GUIDE

AD B=Adductor brevis
AD L=Adductor longus
AD M=Adductor magnus
BF=Biceps femoris
GR=Gracilis
RF=Rectus femoris
SR=Sartorius
ST=Semitendinosus
VM=Vastus medialis
VL=Vastus lateralis
VI=Vastus intermedius

Stand, look down at your right leg, and imagine looking into a slice (cross-section) of your right thigh.

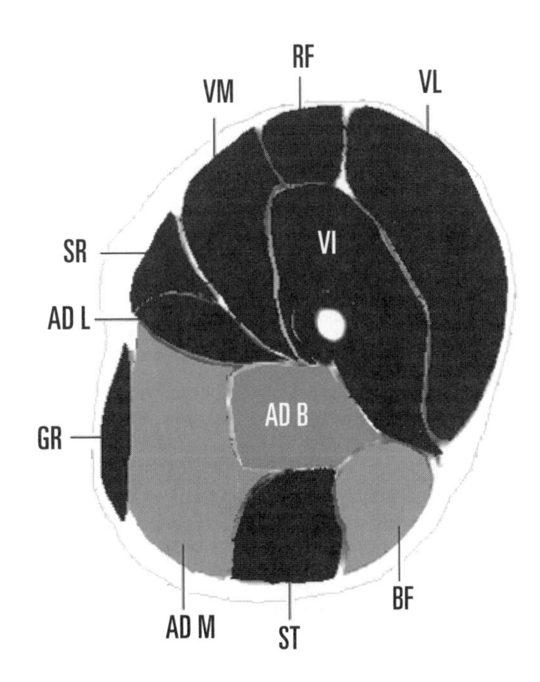

17 SEATED LEG CURL

The idea here is to really isolate the back of the thigh. Obviously, this exercise requires a special machine. There are different versions, but the important thing is to keep the thighs from elevating when your heels pull down on the bar and raise the weight. So push that padded bumper down on the thighs tight. The exercise is done by pulling the heels towards the rump as far as possible, and after a short pause, smoothly allowing the load to pull the lever arm back to the starting position. Be careful at the top not to hyperextend the knee joint. At the same time, it is important to really stretch the back of the thighs and enjoy a full range of motion. Also, keep the ankle joint at about 90 degrees throughout the range of motion.

MUSCLE FUNCTION

The GRACILIS (GR), SARTORIUS (SR) and SEMITENDINOSUS (ST) show marked involvement in this exercise. Surprisingly, the biceps femoris (BF) is not.

GUIDE

AD B=Adductor brevis
AD L=Adductor longus
AD M=Adductor magnus
BF=Biceps femoris
GR=Gracilis
RF=Rectus femoris
SR=Sartorius
ST=Semitendinosus
VM=Vastus medialis
VL=Vastus lateralis
VI=Vastus intermedius

Stand, look down at your right leg, and imagine looking into a slice (cross-section) of your right thigh.

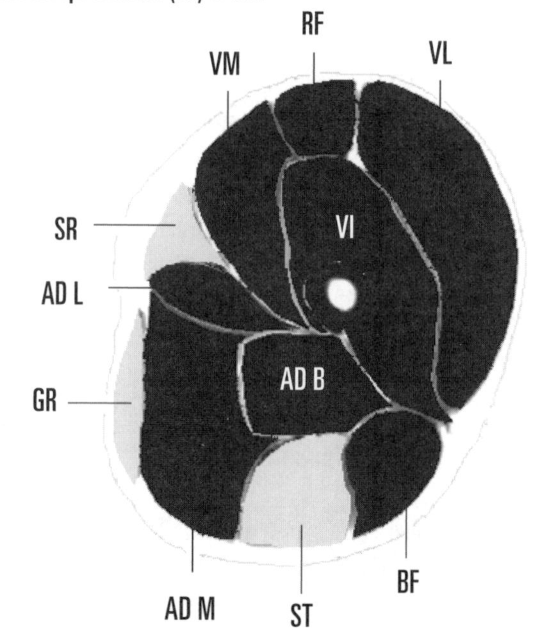

18 SUPINE LEG CURL

To do this, pull your heels towards your rump as far as possible without flexing at the hip joint. That is, keep your rump down. Raise the weight as far as possible, pause, and smoothly let the weight pull the legs back down to the starting position. Oh, feel that stretch. Keep the ankle joints neutral or slightly extended during the exercise.

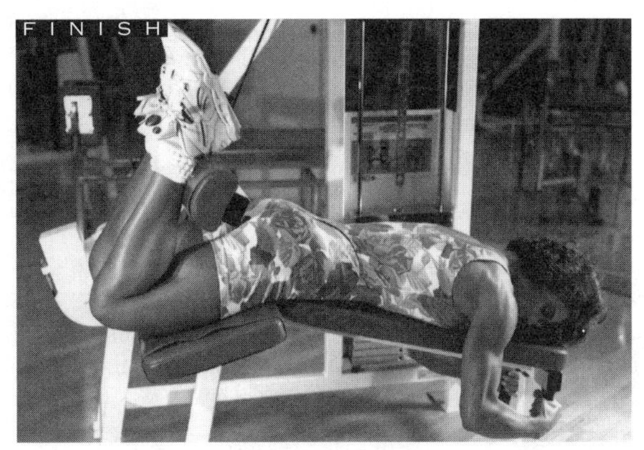

MUSCLE FUNCTION

This is probably the most widely used exercise for the hamstring muscles in the gym. It involves the biceps femoris (BF), semitendinosus (ST), sartorius (SR) and gracilis (GR). They show only moderate use!

GUIDE

AD B=Adductor brevis
AD L=Adductor longus
AD M=Adductor magnus
BF=Biceps femoris
GR=Gracilis
RF=Rectus femoris
SR=Sartorius
ST=Semitendinosus
VM=Vastus medialis
VL=Vastus lateralis
VI=Vastus intermedius

Stand, look down at your right leg, and imagine looking into a slice (cross-section) of your right thigh.

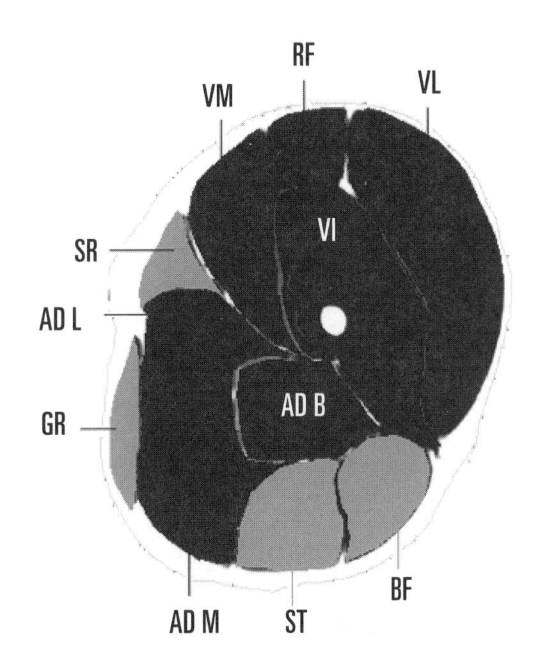

19 ADDUCTION IN MACHINE

The most difficult part of this exercise may be getting into the machine and then making sure your thighs are not stretched too far apart. Oh, what a feeling. The exercise is started with you sitting in the machine, and the legs apart as far as possible. Now, move the hand lever so the mechanical stop will release the weight stack and pull your thighs together. Go all the way, then after a slight pause, relax and let the weight stack pull your thighs back apart. Feel that stretch on the inside of those legs, let it go.

START

MUSCLE FUNCTION

This is an exercise that really isolates one muscle. The ADDUCTOR MAGNUS (AD M) is heavily involved with some support from the gracilis (GR). Evidently, even big boys should be able to benefit from this exercise by adding bulk to the "inside" of the rear thigh.

GUIDE

AD B=Adductor brevis
AD L=Adductor longus
AD M=Adductor magnus
BF=Biceps femoris
GR=Gracilis
RF=Rectus femoris
SR=Sartorius
ST=Semitendinosus
VM=Vastus medialis
VL=Vastus lateralis
VI=Vastus intermedius

Stand, look down at your right leg, and imagine looking into a slice (cross-section) of your right thigh.

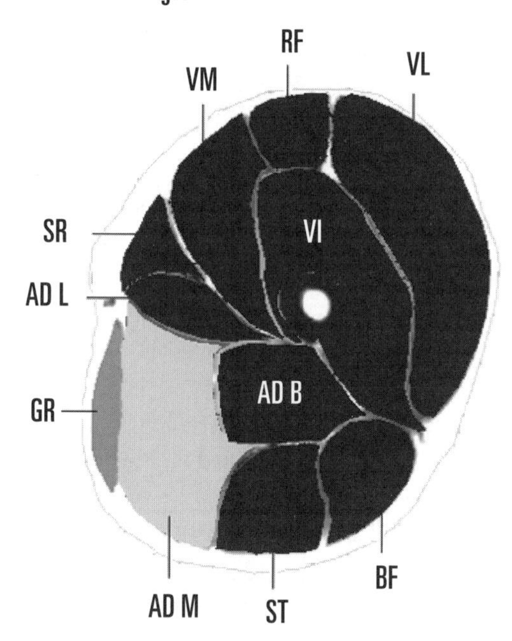

CALF

1 DONKEY CALF RAISE

The idea here is to stand with the balls of the feet elevated, so you can really stretch the calves. In this version of the exercise, the toes point straight forward and the feet are about shoulder width apart. The knees are kept relatively straight and the back slightly arched. The exercise is done by pulling with the calves until you are up on your toes. At the top of the ascent, pause, and then slower lower back down to the starting position. Enjoy a full stretch at the bottom. If you don't have access to a machine like this one, ask your partner to sit on your back; providing extra resistance as in the original Donkeys.

MUSCLE FUNCTION

This calf exercise really taxes the MEDIAL GASTROCNEMIUS (MG). The soleus (SO) and peroneus longus (PL) are moderately involved. You can use a partner sitting on your back instead of a Donkey machine to provide extra load.

GUIDE

SO=Soleus
MG=Medial gastrocnemius
LG=Lateral gastrocnemius
TA=Tibialis anterior
TP=Tibialis posterior
PO=Popliteus
EDL=Extensor digitorum longus
PL=Peroneus longus

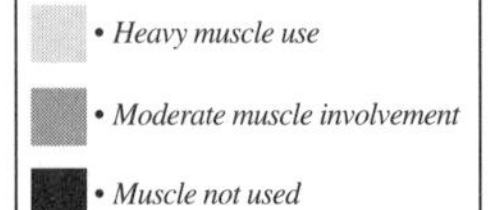

Stand, look down at your left leg, and imagine looking into a slice (cross-section) of your left calf.

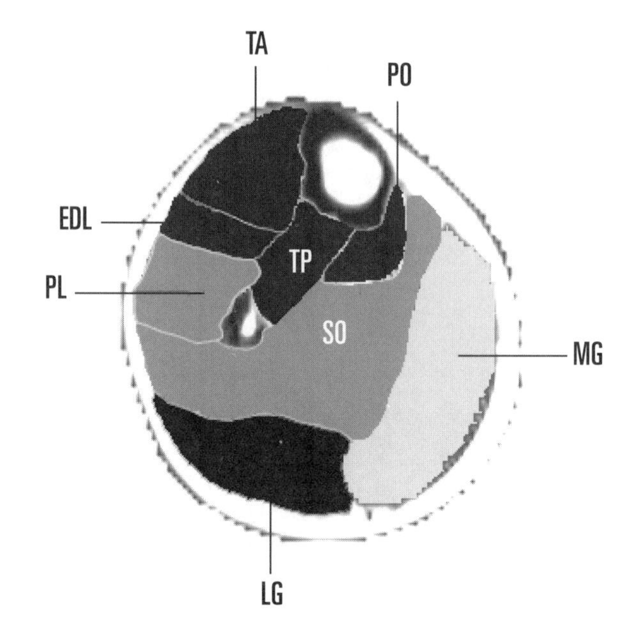

2 DONKEY CALF RAISE *with toes in.*

This exercise is just like #1 except that the toes are pointed inward as far as possible.

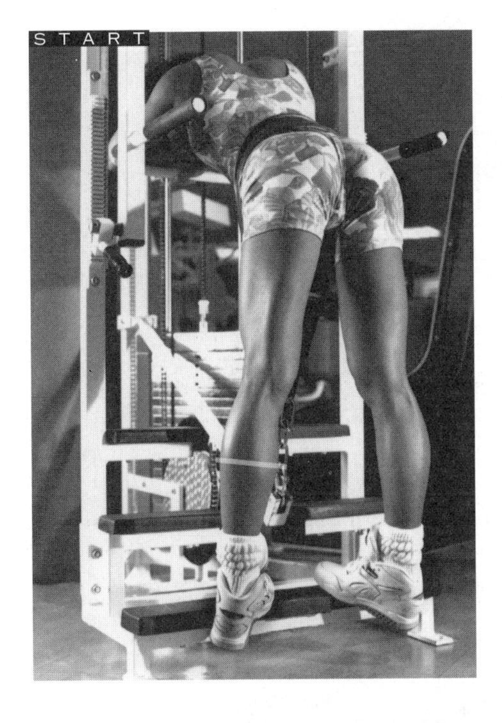

MUSCLE FUNCTION

Performing Donkey raises with the toes rotated in involves the same muscles as doing the exercise with the foot held neutral (#1). The MEDIAL GASTROCNEMIUS (MG) enjoys the most stress, while the soleus (SO) and peroneus longus (PL) show moderate use

GUIDE

SO=Soleus
MG=Medial gastrocnemius
LG=Lateral gastrocnemius
TA=Tibialis anterior
TP=Tibialis posterior
PO=Popliteus
EDL=Extensor digitorum longus
PL=Peroneus longus

Stand, look down at your left leg, and imagine looking into a slice (cross-section) of your left calf.

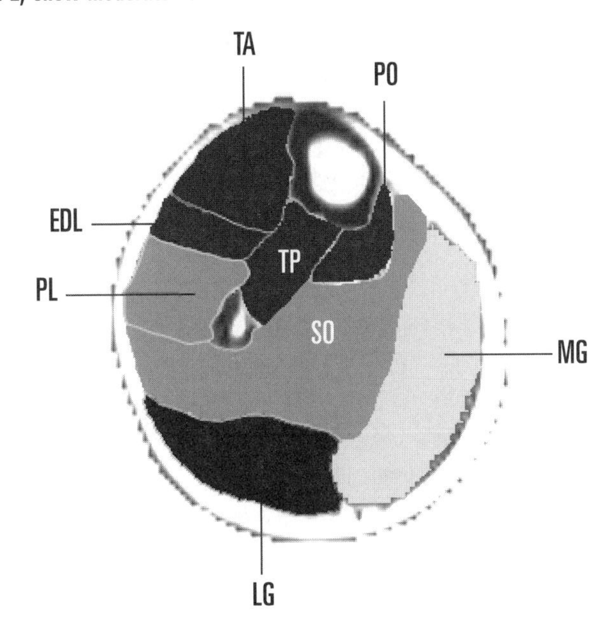

3 DONKEY CALF RAISE *with toes out.*

This exercise is just like #1 and #2 except that the feet are rotated laterally as far as possible, thus the toes point outward.

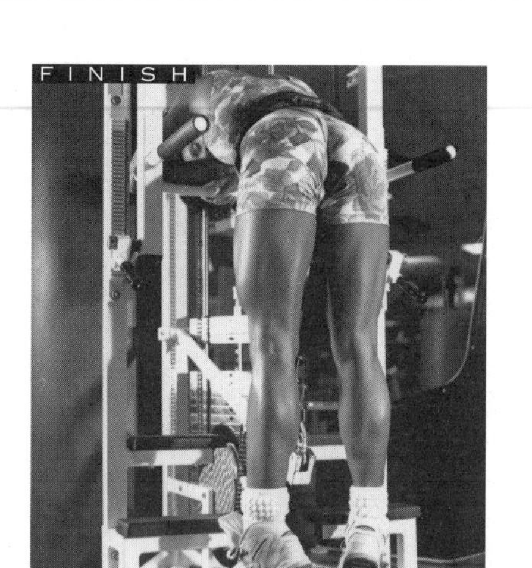

MUSCLE FUNCTION

This calf exercise mainly stresses the MEDIAL GASTROCNEMIUS (MG). The soleus (SO), lateral gastrocnemius (LG) and peroneus longus (PL) are moderately used. Donkey raises, regardless of foot position, always seem to exercise the medial gastrocnemius more than any other muscle.

GUIDE

SO=Soleus
MG=Medial gastrocnemius
LG=Lateral gastrocnemius
TA=Tibialis anterior
TP=Tibialis posterior
PO=Popliteus
EDL=Extensor digitorum longus
PL=Peroneus longus

Stand, look down at your left leg, and imagine looking into a slice (cross-section) of your left calf.

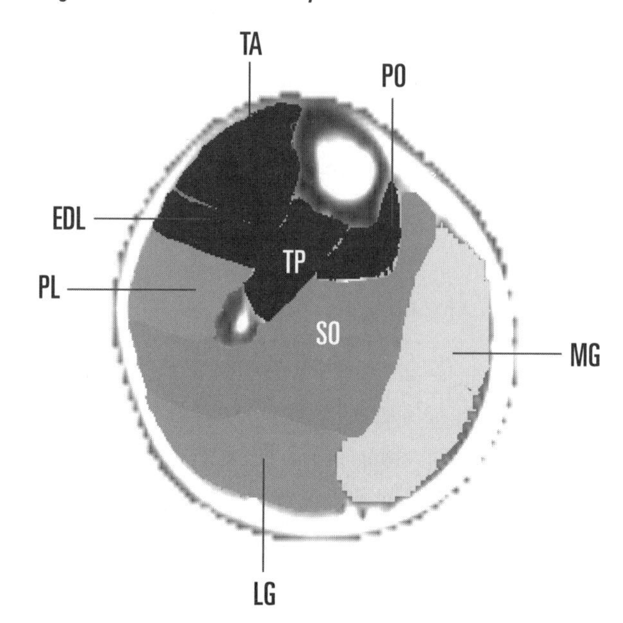

4 STANDING CALF RAISE

This exercise is done with one leg to really stress the calf. Emphasize full stretch when you lower the heel, come to a complete stop and then elevate your body as much as possible with no jerk. The only joint that should show much movement is the ankle joint.

MUSCLE FUNCTION

If you want to get the calf involved - this is the exercise! The MEDIAL and LATERAL GASTROCNEMIUS (MG and LG), SOLEUS (SO) and PERONEUS LONGUS (PL) show marked involvement. Muscle use should be the same if you do this exercise with both legs. If you tend to favor one leg over the other, however, you should do this exercise one leg at a time.

GUIDE

SO=Soleus
MG=Medial gastrocnemius
LG=Lateral gastrocnemius
TA=Tibialis anterior
TP=Tibialis posterior
PO=Popliteus
EDL=Extensor digitorum longus
PL=Peroneus longus

Stand, look down at your left leg, and imagine looking into a slice (cross-section) of your left calf.

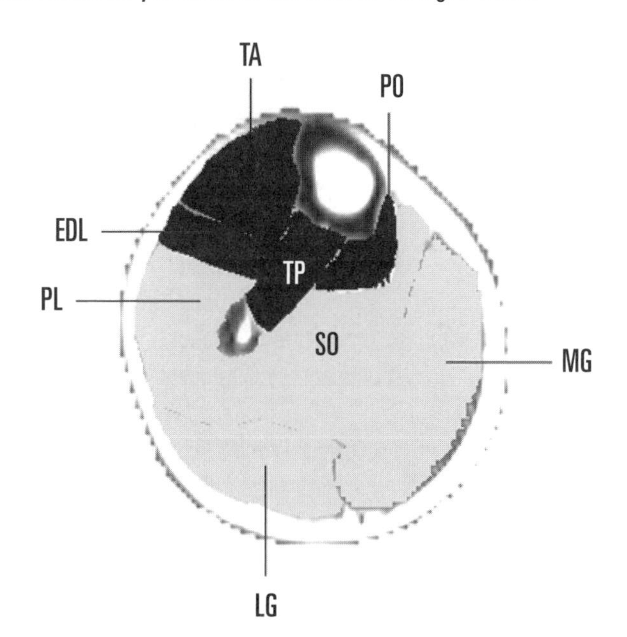

5 STANDING CALF RAISE *with toes in.*

This is like exercise #4. Here, however, both legs are used and extra resistance is provided by using a machine. Moreover, rotate the feet inward as far as possible. Make sure to adjust the shoulder braces so you can enjoy a great stretch at the bottom of the descent without allowing the weights to come to rest on the stack. Remember, the only joints that move are the ankle joints.

MUSCLE FUNCTION

The entire back of calf is involved, but muscle use is only moderate.

GUIDE

SO=Soleus
MG=Medial gastrocnemius
LG=Lateral gastrocnemius
TA=Tibialis anterior
TP=Tibialis posterior
PO=Popliteus
EDL=Extensor digitorum longus
PL=Peroneus longus

Stand, look down at your left leg, and imagine looking into a slice (cross-section) of your left calf.

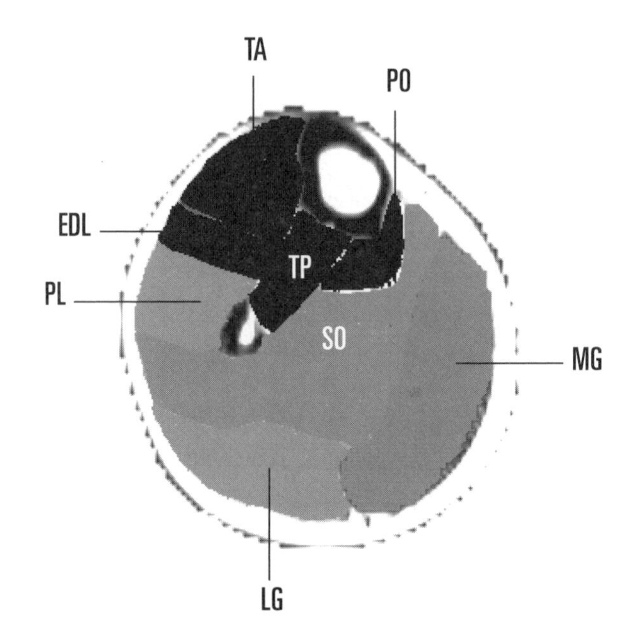

6 STANDING CALF RAISE *with toes out.*

This is exactly like exercise #5, except that the feet are rotated laterally as far as possible so the toes point outward. Now, stretch those calves.

MUSCLE FUNCTION

This exercise seems to be more "effective" than the previous one (#5) which emphasized "toes in". By rotating the feet so that the toes point out, both the SOLEUS (SO) and the MEDIAL GASTROCNEMIUS (MG) enjoy marked stress. The lateral gastrocnemius (LG) and peroneus longus (PL) muscles show moderate use.

GUIDE

SO=Soleus
MG=Medial gastrocnemius
LG=Lateral gastrocnemius
TA=Tibialis anterior
TP=Tibialis posterior
PO=Popliteus
EDL=Extensor digitorum longus
PL=Peroneus longus

Stand, look down at your left leg, and imagine looking into a slice (cross-section) of your left calf.

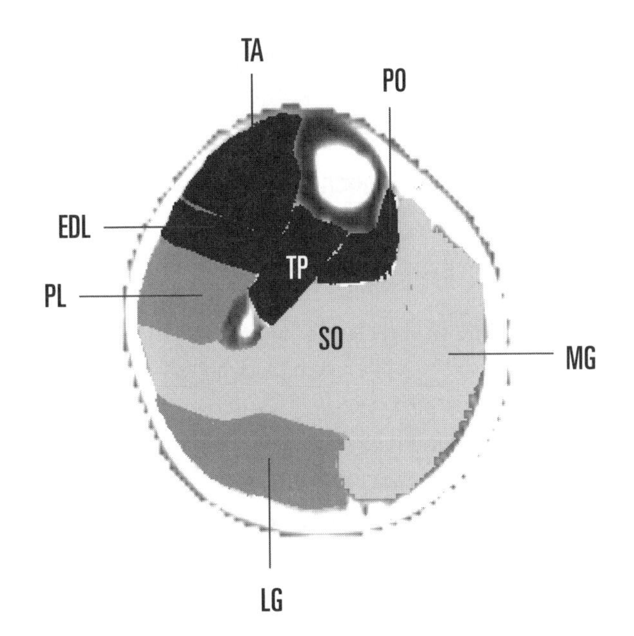

7 CALF RAISE *in Hack machine.*

Using a hack squat machine with a block or a few weight plates on the platform (as shown here), enter the machine reversed so that you face the back support. Place the balls of the feet on the plates, squeeze in under the shoulder pads, and stand erect. Moving only at the ankle joints, raise up on the toes as far as possible, and after a short pause, let the weight push you back down to the starting position.

MUSCLE FUNCTION

This is a great calf exercise. You can hit the MEDIAL GASTROCNEMIUS MG) or SOLEUS (SO) really hard. The outside of the calf, the lateral gastrocnemius (LG) and peroneus longus (PL), is used moderately.

GUIDE

SO=Soleus
MG=Medial gastrocnemius
LG=Lateral gastrocnemius
TA=Tibialis anterior
TP=Tibialis posterior
PO=Popliteus
EDL=Extensor digitorum longus
PL=Peroneus longus

Stand, look down at your left leg, and imagine looking into a slice (cross-section) of your left calf.

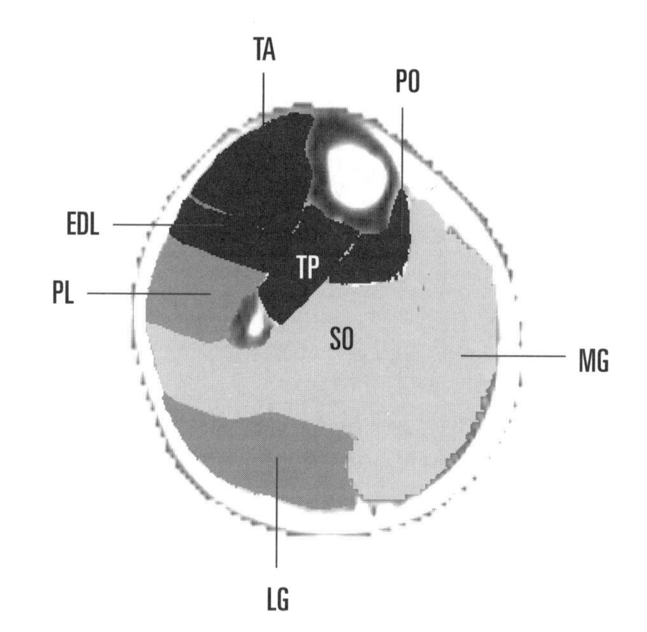

8 SEATED CALF RAISE

So you think you have done enough for those calves. Well, think again. It is time for some seated work. Here, the knee joint is flexed at about 90 degrees to start the exercise. The limiting factor in how far the load is lowered should be your flexibility, not the mechanical stop of the machine. Relax, let it stretch at the bottom. Now, blast those calves and raise the weight as far as possible. In this version of the exercise, the feet are held in the neutral position.

MUSCLE FUNCTION

If you want to get rid of the gastrocnemius (MG and LG) and concentrate on SOLEUS (SO) development, seated calf raise is the exercise. The SOLEUS and somewhat surprisingly the PERONEUS LONGUS (PL) are heavily involved.

GUIDE

SO=Soleus
MG=Medial gastrocnemius
LG=Lateral gastrocnemius
TA=Tibialis anterior
TP=Tibialis posterior
PO=Popliteus
EDL=Extensor digitorum longus
PL=Peroneus longus

Stand, look down at your left leg, and imagine looking into a slice (cross-section) of your left calf.

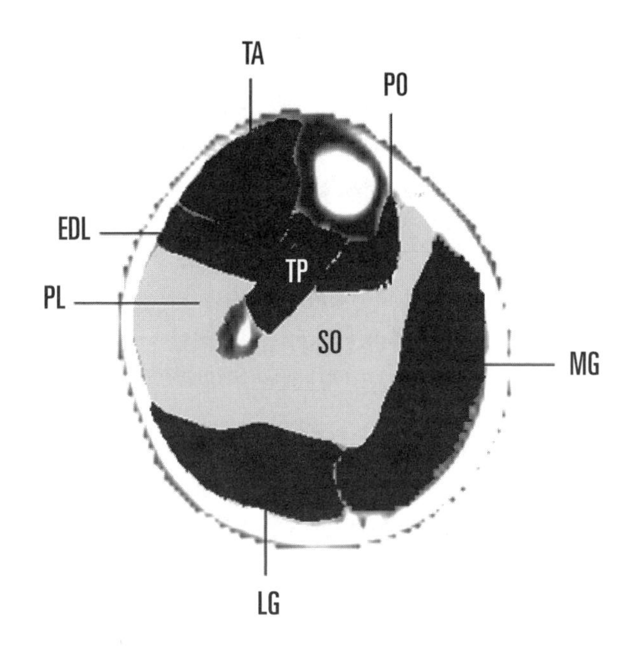

9 SEATED CALF RAISE *with toes in.*

This is just like the preceding exercise (#8), except that the feet are rotated inward as far as possible.

FINISH

START

MUSCLE FUNCTION

This seated calf raise exercise is as effective as the previous one where the feet were in the neutral position. Again, the SOLEUS (SO) and PERONEUS LONGUS (PL) are heavily involved while the gastrocnemius muscle (MG and LG) is silent!

GUIDE

SO=Soleus
MG=Medial gastrocnemius
LG=Lateral gastrocnemius
TA=Tibialis anterior
TP=Tibialis posterior
PO=Popliteus
EDL=Extensor digitorum longus
PL=Peroneus longus

Stand, look down at your left leg, and imagine looking into a slice (cross-section) of your left calf.

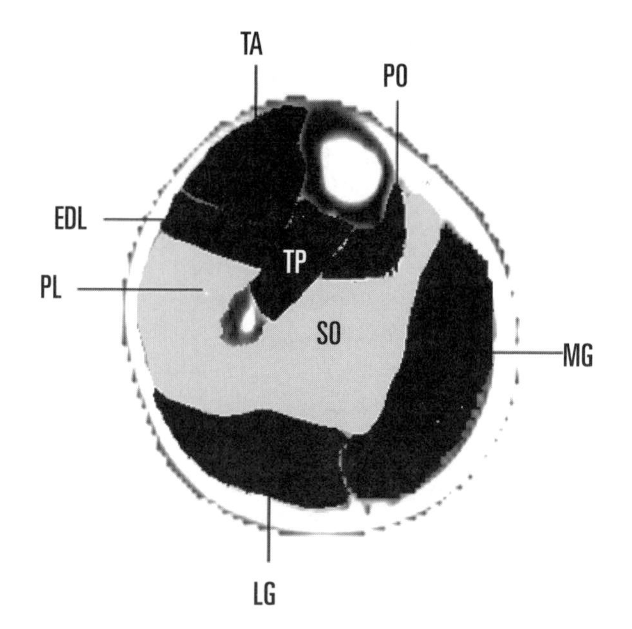

10 SEATED CALF RAISE *with toes out.*

This is just like the preceding exercises (#8, 9), except that the feet are rotated so that toes point outward.

FINISH

START

MUSCLE FUNCTION

Like in the other seated calf exercises (#8, 9), the SOLEUS (SO) and PERONEUS LONGUS (PL) get maximal stress. Muscle use is not influenced by foot position for the seated calf raise. You can do this exercise with the toes pointing in or out or straight ahead - it will pretty much have the same effect!

GUIDE

SO=Soleus
MG=Medial gastrocnemius
LG=Lateral gastrocnemius
TA=Tibialis anterior
TP=Tibialis posterior
PO=Popliteus
EDL=Extensor digitorum longus
PL=Peroneus longus

Stand, look down at your left leg, and imagine looking into a slice (cross-section) of your left calf.

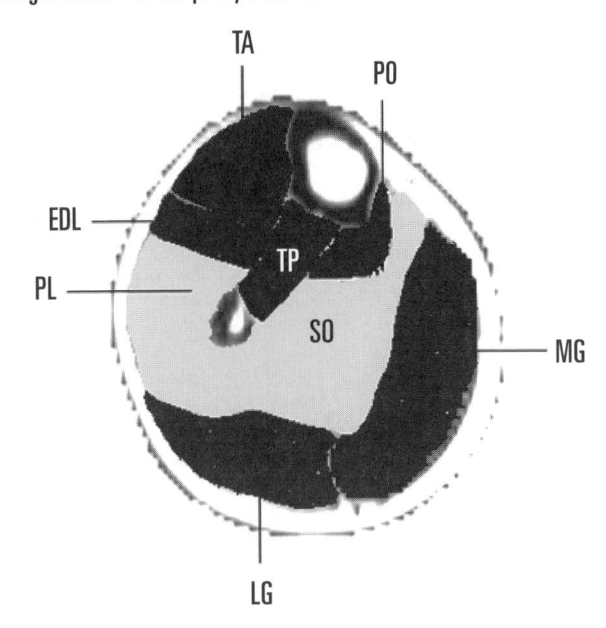

ABOUT THE AUTHOR

Dr. Per A. Tesch is an internationally recognized scientific expert in the field of weightlifting. He is an Associate Professor at the Karolinska Institute in Stockholm, Sweden and has conducted numerous scientific research studies on skeletal muscle adaptations to weight lifting over the past decade. His work has been published in the most prestigious scientific journals. Dr. Tesch has given invited speeches at international scientific meetings and has been awarded grant funds from several renowned agencies to conduct research work. Among others, he has worked with the Swedish Sports Federation, NASA, the European Space Agency and the US Army Research Institute. He has also been funded by such highly regarded institutions as the Royal Swedish Air Force and the National Strength and Conditioning Association. He is a Fellow of the American College of Sports Medicine and a regular writer for international sports magazines such as Muscle and Fitness.

After all this work, the author felt something really important was missing from his work and his understanding of weight lifting. No one really knew which muscles were actually used to do a certain exercise. It was not long, however, before he realized that the complicated technology of magnetic resonance imaging could be used to fill this major gap in our appreciation of weight lifting. And you are the one that will benefit. MUSCLE MEETS MAGNET clearly shows you which individual arm and leg muscles are used to do over 60 different bodybuilding exercises.

DAILY WORKOUT TRAINING LOG

Make copies of this chart and save in a looseleaf binder or folder. Use one sheet per day.

BODYPART	EXERCISE	SETS	REPS	WEIGHT USED

*Date*________________________

*Week Ending*____________________

M T W TH F S S

Circle day of the week

MRI

DAILY WORKOUT TRAINING LOG

Make copies of this chart and save in a looseleaf binder or folder. Use one sheet per day.

BODYPART	EXERCISE	SETS	REPS	WEIGHT USED

*Date*______________________________

*Week Ending*__________________________

M T W TH F S S

Circle day of the week

DAILY WORKOUT TRAINING LOG

Make copies of this chart and save in a looseleaf binder or folder. Use one sheet per day.

BODYPART	EXERCISE	SETS	REPS	WEIGHT USED

*Date*______________________________ M T W TH F S S

*Week Ending*________________________ *Circle day of the week*

MRI